RURAL DISTRICT

IN GLOUCESTERSHIRE

1880-1925

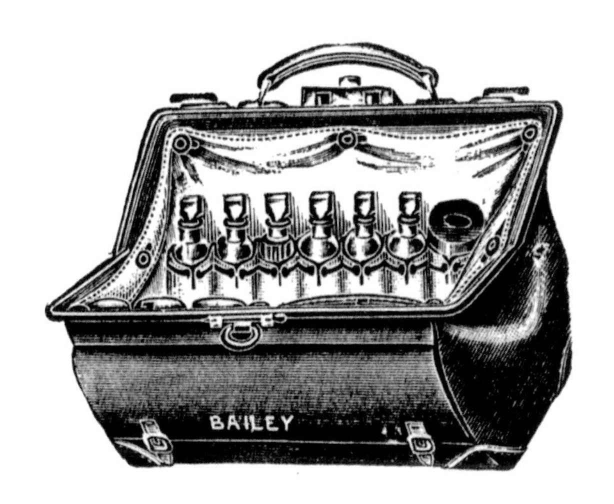

Carrie Howse

Published by
REARDON PUBLISHING
PO Box 919, Cheltenham, Glos, GL50 9AN.
Website: www.reardon.co.uk

Written and Compiled
by
Carrie Howse

Layout and Design
by
Nicholas Reardon

ISBN 1 873877 8 54
ISBN (13) 9781873877852

Photographs reproduced by courtesy of
Gloucestershire Archives

Printed in China Through
World Print Ltd

CONTENTS

INTRODUCTION

Ask anyone to name a Victorian pioneer of nursing reform and the answer will probably be, "Florence Nightingale". Few people have heard of her contemporary, Elizabeth Malleson (1828-1916), founder of the Rural Nursing Association (RNA), or realise the importance of Gloucestershire as the place where her national system of rural district nursing began.

This book, which began life as a PhD thesis (University of Gloucestershire, 2004), traces the development of trained district nursing in rural Gloucestershire from the 1880s, when Elizabeth Malleson moved to the area from London, until 1925, when the first State Registration examinations were held and a new era began for the entire nursing profession. The transition from local provision of aid by untrained women to the organised delivery of care by specially trained nurses employed by the RNA is described, and the expansion of this local charity into a national scheme is traced to its affiliation and eventual amalgamation with Queen Victoria's Jubilee Institute for Nurses (QVJI), the organisation from which today's system of district nursing has evolved.

Florence Nightingale believed that the future of nursing lay in district nursing, with its dual aims of curative care and preventative education, but historians of British nursing (e.g. Abel-Smith, 1960, and Maggs, 1983) tend to concentrate on general nursing in the hospital setting, as that is where training took place. District nursing, if it is mentioned at all in such studies, is seen as only a footnote to the broader context of social history and philanthropy, instead of being recognised as central to pre-NHS welfare policies. The only official histories of district nursing were written by Mary Stocks and Monica Baly in 1960 and 1987, respectively, and these two slim volumes remain the main sources on QVJI, the central body that standardised training and unified existing philanthropic schemes through its system of affiliation and inspection. Baly uses Stocks as her main secondary source, and whilst both books are factual and informative, their scope is limited by the fact that they were commissioned to celebrate milestones in the history of district nursing. They are, therefore, designed to be congratulatory and to emphasise positive progress over the years. They concentrate on the leading figures of the movement, not on the nurses themselves, and on details of politics and administration, not on the day-to-day duties and problems involved in nursing the sick poor in their own homes.

It is the aim of this book to help redress this imbalance in the historiography of nursing by examining the change from traditional benevolence to the provision of professional nursing care in rural Gloucestershire through the lives of and relationships between three tiers of local society: the middle and upper class ladies who devoted years of their lives to the administration and management of the rural district nursing system, entirely on a voluntary basis; the specially trained nurses who delivered the care; and the poor patients who benefited from it. To this end, the aims and motivation of the lady administrators are considered, with particular reference to religion, politics and the opportunity to expand their lives beyond the limited role prescribed for them by the cult of domesticity. The official aims of the district nurses themselves are traced, and theory and practice are then compared and contrasted. The working lives of the district nurses are described, including their duties, workload, salaries and living conditions, with additional reference to the contemporary ideologies of 'fit work for women', social isolation versus independence, and relationships with administrators and local doctors. Consideration is also given to the question of whether the service provided by those who believed that they knew what the sick poor needed was, in fact, what the poor themselves actually wanted. To this end, the educative aims of QVJI are examined in comparison with two of the most fundamental and sustaining elements of life amongst the poor, especially in isolated rural communities - neighbourliness and intergenerational support.

By combining the quantitative data from surviving local and national records with the qualitative interpretation of the human interaction between the lady administrators, the district nurses and their poor patients in Gloucestershire, it is hoped that this book will provide a valuable addition, not only to a neglected area of the history of nursing in particular, but also to local, social and women's history in general.

It would not have been possible to complete the original PhD thesis without kind and generous funding from the Macfarlane Walker Trust. Thanks for advice and help are due to: the staff at the Gloucestershire Record Office and Cheltenham Reference Library; Dr Anne Summers of the British Library; Helen Wakely of the Contemporary Medical Archives Centre; Maggie Wheel of Inter-library Loans at the University of Gloucestershire; Mary Southerton, Jane Sale and Mary Paget of the Charlton Kings Local History Society; Lord St Aldwyn, for access to the private family papers of Lady Lucy Hicks-Beach, and Maggie James of the Williamstrip Park Estate Office who located and photocopied the papers.

Special thanks are due to my friend Hazel Parris, who, with great enthusiasm and efficiency, copied records from the Queen's Roll for me; to my PhD Supervisors, Dr Melanie Ilic of the University of Gloucestershire, and Professor Diana Woodward of Napier University, Edinburgh, for their advice, help, encouragement and support; and last, but certainly not least, to my son, Simon, whose computer skills have been invaluable.

Finally, this book is dedicated, with love, to my friend Susanne McKenna, who never lost faith in the VCM.

Note

The title Queen Victoria's Jubilee Institute for Nurses was changed in 1928 to the Queen's Institute of District Nursing and later still to the Queen's Nursing Institute. Throughout this book, which covers the years 1880 to 1925, the original title is used.

Pre-decimal currency

12 pence (12d.)	=	1 shilling (1s.)
20 shillings (20s.)	=	1 pound (£1)

2s. = 10p.

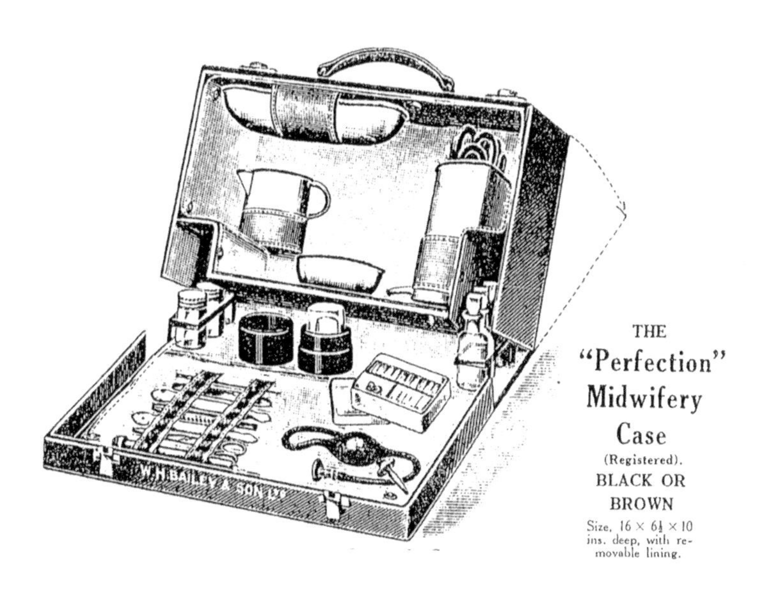

The development of rural district nursing

Date	Rural	Urban
1860s		William Rathbone sets up district nursing scheme in Liverpool.
1875		William Rathbone and Florence Nightingale form The Metropolitan Nursing Association in London.
1884	Elizabeth Malleson founds local Village Nursing Association in Gotherington, Gloucestershire.	
1889		Queen Victoria's Jubilee Institute for Nurses established.
1890	Elizabeth Malleson founds national Rural Nursing Association.	
1891-2	RNA affiliated to QVJI as its Rural District Branch.	
1897	Amalgamation between urban and rural branches of QVJI.	

Organisational structure of QVJI

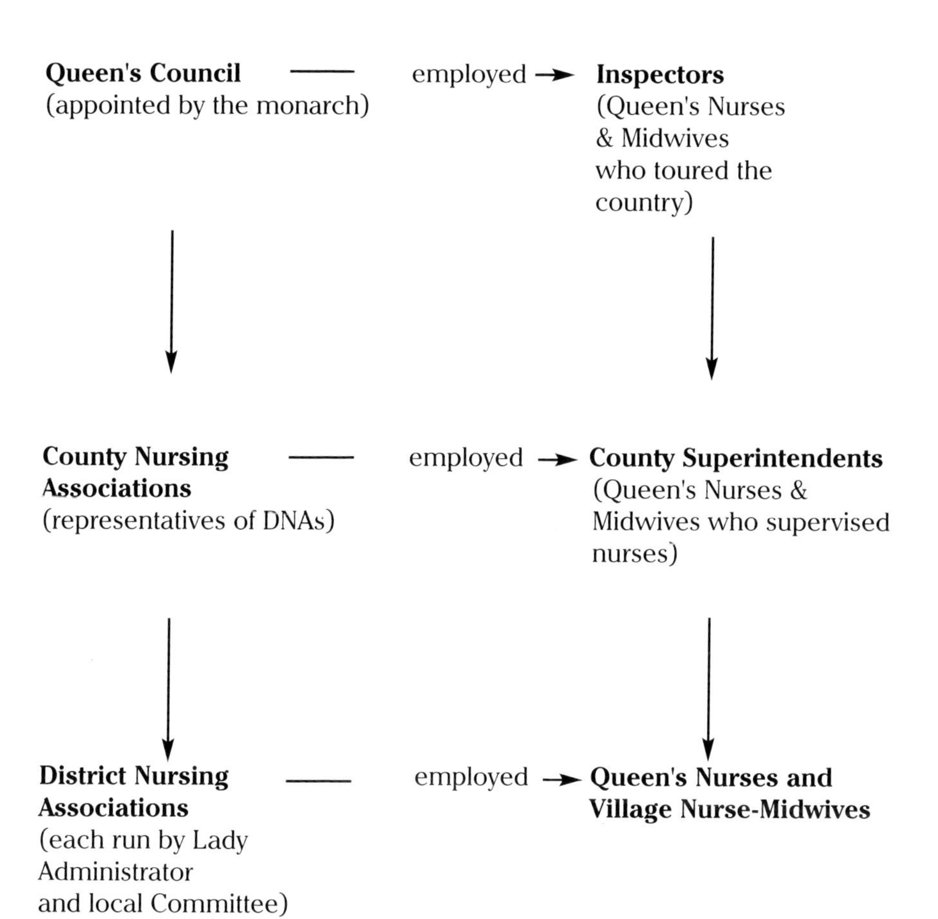

CHAPTER ONE
HEALTH CARE IN THE 1880s

Institutional care

By the 1880s, Florence Nightingale's reforms of the nursing system had clearly had an effect on hospitals throughout England, despite the entrenched views and professional jealousy of some doctors, who expressed their disapproval in the pages of the *Lancet* and the *British Medical Journal*.[1] Nursing had progressed from being an occupation exclusively for working class women to a respectable and worthy profession for women of all social classes. However, conditions in hospitals continued to vary, as there was still no standard training nor a national register. Individual hospitals still issued their own certificates, either to working class girls who trained for two to four years, depending on the hospital, or to 'lady' pupils who paid £1 a week each for a year's tuition, at a time when the average weekly wage for a male agricultural labourer was only 13s.9d.

Demographic changes had resulted in an ever-increasing number of such ladies from the middle and upper classes who needed to work. The census of 1881 recorded more than 13 million women in England and Wales, compared with 12.5 million men. In the overall population, there were 1,055 women to every 1,000 men, whilst in the economically productive age group of 20-44, the ratio was 1,083 per 1,000. This disproportion between the sexes was greater among the middle classes than the working classes as increasing numbers of their young men emigrated to work throughout the British Empire and beyond, and consequently either postponed or abstained from marriage. As a result, the 'superfluous women', as they became known, needed to find work to support themselves not just for a few years until they married, but for their entire lives. The demographic changes therefore coincided with the reform of nursing, creating a pool of potential labour of precisely the calibre which Florence Nightingale aimed to attract. The 'lady' probationers' ability to pay for their training not only provided an important source of income for the hospitals, which were all funded by voluntary contributions at this time, but also suggested that entering the profession was considered to be so commendable that it was worth paying to be trained. This, itself, further raised the status of nursing, which in turn then attracted more recruits from the middle and upper classes.[2]

The need for trained, educated nurses was an integral part of medical progress. It both arose from and reflected a change in the philosophy and goals of medical treatment from relief of suffering to cure, which itself derived from contemporary scientific discoveries. Chloroform became the most widely used anaesthetic, in preference to ether, after it was first introduced in medical practice by Sir James Simpson in 1847, and as operations became more extensive and successful, so the post-operative nursing needs of the patients increased. From the 1860s, the application of Lister's antiseptic principles, based on Pasteur's germ theory of disease, not only reduced surgical mortality rates from between 25-40% in 1865 to approximately 4% in 1890, but also further developed nurses' technical skills in aseptic techniques and more and improved dressings. Germ theory and the control of infection developed further in 1876 when Robert Koch identified the function of bacteria in the disease process. As a result of such scientific and medical advances in the latter half of the nineteenth century, doctors increasingly had to rely on the skilled care and observation of the nurses, who were in constant attendance on the patients, in contrast to the doctors' own intermittent visits to the wards.[3]

These improvements were reflected in hospital data, both nationally and locally. At Cheltenham Hospital in 1880, a total of 629 'in-door' patients were admitted, "409 of whom were discharged cured, and 161 relieved". The average number of patients in the hospital at any one time was 63.86 and the average time each patient remained on a ward was 38.07 days. The 99 surgical operations performed that year included 19 amputations, from which two patients died of shock. Amongst the medical patients, the most commonly treated conditions were 32 cases of rheumatism, of which 28 were cured and 4 relieved; 18 cases of anaemia, all cured; 13 skin ulcers, 12 cured, 1 unrelieved; 13 cases of pneumonia, 10 cured, 1 relieved, 2 died; 8 cases of bronchitis, all cured; and 8 cases of heart disease, 4 cured, 4 died. Overall, it was reported that "the deaths in the Hospital have been greater in number this year than usual, amounting in all to 37, 14 of which were the results of accidents". When these 14 fatal accidents are discounted, the death rate amongst patients in 1880 falls from 5.88% to 3.66%, which compares favourably with 3.94% in 1879 and 3.1% in 1878.[4]

Yet, despite such results, hospitals remained institutions which cared primarily for the urban poor. The more prosperous classes continued to be nursed privately at home and entered hospitals only as charitable visitors, inspectors or governors.

In many rural areas, there were no hospitals and it was to combat this problem that Cottage Hospitals were established, the first being founded in 1859 by Mr Albert Napper MRCS at Cranleigh in Surrey. As the name suggests, the earliest of these hospitals were set up in converted cottages where a resident nurse provided care for four to ten patients and a general practitioner paid regular visits. Over the years, many such hospitals were extended or moved to new, purpose-built premises, "resulting from the absolute necessity of providing better accommodation for the poor in cases of sickness or accident than that afforded in their own homes". Bourton-on-the-Water Cottage Hospital was only the third such hospital to be established in England, when Dr John Moore leased Buryfield Cottage in 1861. A new building was erected on a different site in 1879, and was in turn succeeded by a new hospital in 1928.[5]

Miss Rebecca Horne, the first Matron of Moreton-in-Marsh Cottage Hospital has left her recollections of its foundation in the 1870s when "Dr Leonard Yelf was attending my friend Miss Challis, in my home, during a long illness and being (I suppose) pleased with my nursing, he said how much he wished he could get a bed in some cottage, which he could use for some poor patient." He approached a local patron, Lord Redesdale, who generously offered a site for a small hospital and £150 towards the building costs. Whilst the hospital was under construction, Miss Horne joined a group of nurses at Winchester, who were being trained there by the Nightingale Fund, which illustrates that, although the hospital was envisaged primarily as providing respite care, the nursing was expected to be of a high standard. The new hospital was opened by the Bishop of Gloucester on 24 July 1873 and the first two patients were admitted four days later. Miss Horne recalls, "20 others followed before the end of the year and only one of those was 'ulcer of leg' thus disproving the prophecy of a friend (who afterwards became an energetic helper in the Hospital) who said we should never get any patients except old women with bad legs!"[6]

The willingness of a local patron to fund a new purpose-built hospital, instead of merely converting a cottage, reflects the growing awareness of the need to make provision for rural patients who could not afford private nursing at home, but whose condition was not serious enough to warrant removal to an urban hospital. The criteria for admission were clearly set out in the Rules of Fairford Cottage Hospital, founded in 1867, which state that, "The Hospital is designed for the benefit and accommodation of the poor when suffering from Disease or Accident; but no case of Infectious or Contagious Disease, or of Pulmonary Consumption, shall be admissable." All costs and expenses were met by charitable donations and subscriptions, but patients were "required to pay towards their maintenance a weekly sum, the amount of which, dependent upon circumstances, shall be decided upon by the Committee in conjunction with the Patient's Employers, or with the Poor Law Authorities". In 1880, subscriptions totalled £61.11s.6d., with a further £23.5s.9d. raised through collections in local churches and chapels, whilst payments received from patients, ranging from 2s.6d. upwards, totalled only 12s.0d. Applications for admission to the hospital, accompanied by a Letter of Recommendation from a subscriber, were considered by the Committee and Medical Officer at their Monthly Meetings, except for cases of accident or emergency. Subscribers of £1 or more annually were able to recommend one patient to be admitted free of charge per year. A total of 23 patients were admitted during 1880, ranging from a 3 year old boy with "Bladder Irritation" to a 68 year old woman with "Injury to Hip". Each patient spent an average of 20.2 days in hospital and 20 were eventually discharged cured, whilst the other three were either relieved or improved. The emphasis appears to have been on a nourishing diet and rest rather than medical treatment, as the total cost of Provisions was £35.6s.7d., with an additional £3.8s.5d. for Beer, Wine & Spirits, but only £7.3s.0d. was spent on Medical & Surgical Appliances.[7]

Similarly, Tetbury Cottage Hospital, established in 1868, treated 39 patients during 1880, with an average duration of stay of 24 days. Total Food & Maintenance costs amounted to £43.15s.10d., plus £1.19s.6d. for Wine & Beer, and only £16.0s.11d. for Medicines & Surgical Appliances. At Bourton-on-the-Water, 44 patients were treated in 1880, with a daily average of 4 beds occupied and an average stay of 36 days. Provisions cost £57.19s.8d., with Wine, Beer &c £7.12s.6d., whilst £11.4s.3d. was spent on Drugs & Instruments.[8]

By 1870, some 70 Cottage Hospitals had been established throughout the country and by 1880 the number was nearer 300. Where they existed, the respite care they provided was no doubt beneficial and welcome, but many poor country dwellers still had to resort to the infirmary ward of the local workhouse.

The Poor Law Amendment Act of 1834 had been designed to discourage pauperism, and thus reduce the financial burden on the ratepayers, by making conditions in workhouses so strict, harsh and comfortless that only the desperate would seek relief within their walls. Thus, able-bodied paupers would be encouraged to find work and support themselves. However, this approach assumed that work was available, if only the poor would look for it, and genuinely destitute families were demoralised and humiliated by seeking the help they needed.

The replacement of the Poor Law Board by the Local Government Board, under the Act of 1871, brought public health into the same administrative department as poor relief. The subsequent series of Acts during the 1870s, which consolidated previous attempts at sanitary reform, also saw the appointment of Medical Officers of Health responsible for effecting national policies at local level. This was a clear indication that the state should accept responsibility for the health of the people, including provision for the sick poor. The Metropolitan Poor Act of 1867, prompted by Florence Nightingale's determined campaign for workhouse reform, had already established that the sick should be separated from the able-bodied paupers, and under the Local Government Board, arrangements were made to allow workhouses to admit and train probationer nurses on their infirmary wards. Furthermore, the Medical Relief (Disqualification Removal) Act of 1885 was designed to end the stigma of pauperism attached to appeals to the Local Government Board. Nevertheless, admission to the workhouse was still regarded by the poor with a sense of dread and humiliation, as Flora Thompson poignantly conveys in her memoirs of her Oxfordshire childhood, when she describes the removal of an elderly neighbour to the workhouse: "As soon as he realized where he was being taken, the old soldier, the independent old bachelor, the kind family friend, collapsed and cried like a child."[9]

Nurses in workhouses still tended to be working class women, each nurse attending an average of twenty patients. At Winchcombe Union Workhouse in 1880, a typical weekly report shows that out of a total of 54 inmates, 33 men and 10 women were classified as "old & infirm" and therefore in need of nursing care.[10]

Conditions for able-bodied inmates were still notoriously harsh throughout the 1880s, as entries in the Punishment Books for the workhouses at Tewkesbury and Chipping Sodbury testify. Offences such as using obscene language, violent behaviour, refusing to obey orders and neglecting work were all punished by being locked up for anything between one and twenty-four hours, with between one and six meals of bread and water. At Chipping Sodbury, no less than 12 entries were made concerning Julia Lawrence, a 25 year old single woman from Yate, the first reading: "Disturbing the inmates of the female ward, continually persisting in using profane language. Ill-using her infant (aged about 9 weeks) by knocking its head against the cot, and throwing it on the ground in the yard. Also threatening to kill her infant." As a result, she was "locked up 6 hrs" and fed on "bread and water for 3 days over Christmas" in 1881. The following year, she was punished 8 times, all for persistent quarrelling and fighting and abuse of her baby. At Tewkesbury, Mary-Ann Beesley was "confined in Bedroom 8 hours and birched by Matron" for "Disrespect at Divine Service & Disobedience", whilst three boys were "flogged by the Master" for stealing potatoes, Emma Musto was given three meals of bread and water when "found talking to one of the male inmates" and George Pool was "taken before the Magistrate and was committed to Gloucester Prison for 14 days" for "having indecent connection with a female inmate".[11]

Such an atmosphere could hardly have been conducive to the rest, peace and quiet needed by the older and infirm inmates. However, at Stroud Workhouse in 1880, the Chaplain, who visited twice weekly, reported that "the general management of the house under the able supervision and kindly considerations of the Master and Matron is such that must tend towards the general comfort and wellbeing of the inmates". It was "a source of much comfort" to him "to find that the new nurse ... takes much pains to alleviate the sufferings of the sick" and he appealed to the Guardians to assist him "to form a good library especially for the sick". At Winchcombe in December 1880, the Master begged "to call the attention of the Board to the near approach of Christmas and to ask leave to provide the usual Christmas dinner of roast beef and plum pudding for the inmates of the House".[12]

On appearing before the Board to be discharged from the workhouse, inmates were often allowed between 1s. and 2s.6d., the lower amount sometimes accompanied by one or two loaves, described as "a little relief on leaving the House". Nor was the departure of patients prematurely hastened. At Winchcombe, during the first half of 1880, one man aged 61 was refused permission to leave, whilst a 21 year old man was "advised to remain another week".[13]

Out-relief prescribed by Medical Officers still relied heavily on treatment in kind in 1880, with food taking precedence over medicines. At Tetbury, the most commonly ordered "Necessaries to be given to the Patient" consisted of meat, sometimes as much as two pounds in weight, prescribed for patients as diverse as a ten year old girl with "catarrh & debility", a 20 year old woman with "debility after miscarriage" and an 80 year old man with bronchitis, plus cases of peritonitis, dyspepsia, rheumatism, cardiac disease, carcinoma, epilepsy, paralysis and a fractured leg. One pint of milk per day was prescribed for a 1½ year old child and a 27 year old man, both with bronchitis, and for an 18 year old man with "Hip disease". Brandy was occasionally ordered for bronchitis and carcinoma, and for a 70 year old woman with diarrhoea, whilst one 28 year old woman "in a state of debility following childbirth" was given both meat and wine. Such treatment might appear totally inadequate to deal with the illnesses concerned, but 'atrophy' or 'wasting' disorders, caused by poor diet, still accounted for approximately 20% of all infant deaths in rural areas towards the end of the nineteenth century; therefore, treatment in kind could at least help to compensate for general dietary deficiencies.[14]

Whilst such measures were clearly of some benefit, any form of institutional care was still regarded with fear by the rural poor, who generally preferred to rely on traditional remedies administered at home.

Patent and folk medicines

Among children in rural areas, as in the towns, dysentery, enteritis and diarrhoea were major causes of death. Of the epidemic diseases, compulsory vaccination had reduced the annual mortality rate from smallpox from 2.73 per 1,000 children up to the age of four in 1839 to 0.1 per 1,000 in country districts between 1873 and '77. However, typhoid, diphtheria, scarlet fever, whooping cough and measles continued to take their toll, and the overcrowded, unhygienic conditions of many rural homes encouraged the spread of such illnesses.[15]

For all ages, respiratory diseases, particularly tuberculosis, bronchitis and pneumonia, were common and greatly feared. Among older people, rheumatism was rife, and in many country areas, elderly villagers took opium in one of its varied forms to relieve their pain. Amongst the rural poor, there was still a strong reliance on such folk and herbal medicine, based on ingredients which could easily be grown or gathered in the countryside, such as poppy heads for infusion as poppy head tea, one of the opiate remedies.[16]

Few families could afford a doctor's fees and not all practitioners were sympathetic towards the poor. One young Gloucestershire woman died giving birth to illegitimate twins when the local doctor refused to attend:

> The midwife engaged by the girl's father found the case difficult throughout the night and so at 7.30a.m. the girl's father went to fetch the Parish Poor Law Medical Officer who lived about three miles away. The father had no Poor-relief Order and no means of paying privately so Mr Cooke refused to attend. At 5p.m. the father persuaded a Mr Wood of Ledbury, four miles away, to attend his daughter. When he arrived the mother and both babies were dead.

Reporting the case and the subsequent Coroner's enquiry, the *Lancet* dismissed "claptrap charges of inhumanity" and concluded that, "Mr Cooke is a gentleman who has been more than 40 years in practice, and ... he cannot be expected to be at the beck and call of every girl who has the misfortune to have an illegitimate child".[17]

There were, of course, doctors who were more charitable towards the poor, but in many rural areas, medical practitioners were feared and avoided as much as institutional care.

One alternative was the local town pharmacists, who practised in direct competition with doctors. Before the introduction of national health insurance in 1911, pharmacists rarely saw a doctor's prescription, as 90% of all dispensing took place in the doctor's own surgery. Pharmacists prepared and prescribed their own remedies, as well as making-up family recipes for their predominantly working and lower-middle class clientele. Walwins of Gloucester prepared an average of 150 prescriptions per month during 1880, including two issued on Christmas Day. Unfortunately, the conditions being treated were not recorded, but the ingredients most commonly used in recipes were morphine (an analgesic), digitalis (a heart stimulant), belladonna (for its antispasmodic properties), arsenic (mixed with iron as a tonic, or on its own as treatment for syphilis), bromide (a hypnotic depressant), and strychnine (a nerve and muscle stimulant, used in tonics). Both Sellors of Tewkesbury and Thompson of Tetbury prepared treatments for farm animals as well as humans, using similar ingredients for both, and many orders were sent by handwritten notes as part of domestic errands: "Mr Thompson will you please to send Soda Water Powders by the butcher Saturday"; "Please send to The Vicarage by bearer 1 Box Antipyrine Powders."[18]

In addition to freshly prepared recipes, ready-made patent medicines were becoming increasingly available, not only in chemists but also in grocers' and general stores, and were widely advertised in periodicals. These, too, had their roots in tradition: Thomas Beecham and Jesse Boot both had strong connections with folk medicine and medical botany. In Lark Rise, Flora Thompson recalls, "Beecham's and Holloway's Pills were already familiar to all newspaper readers, and a booklet advertising Mother Siegel's Syrup arrived by post at every house once a year. But only Beecham's Pills were patronized, and those only by a few." Beecham's Pills were also regularly advertised in the *Cheltenham Examiner* as a twenty minute cure for "Bilious and Nervous Disorders", as well as euphemistically "removing any obstruction or irregularity of the system ... for Females of all ages". This was a widely understood code amongst women of all classes, as was its most famous advertising slogan 'Worth a Guinea a Box', the same price as a back-street abortion. Its reputation as an abortifacient was based on a widespread belief that the pills contained lead. This was, in fact, untrue, but it remained a powerful myth that boosted sales.[19]

As the nineteenth century progressed, cure-all remedies, advertised in both the local and cheap national press, became a booming business and many of them made increasingly unrealistic claims of scientific prowess. Willis of Gloucester claimed in the *Cheltenham Examiner* that his Condensed Extract of Sarsaparilla and Quinine would "purify the system" and prolong life; Beetham & Co of Cheltenham offered its own brand of Hair Fluid "of world-wide celebrity ... as used by many of the Ladies and Gentlemen at the Court of Her Majesty, and thousands of the Nobility and Gentry", whilst its Corn & Bunion Plasters were "acknowledged by upwards of 5,000 persons to be the most wonderful production of the age".[20]

However, urban outlets were often beyond the reach of the rural poor and commercially produced remedies were more expensive than those made at home or prepared by the local 'old wife'. Such women, who acted as both untrained nurses and midwives, are traditionally characterised as unhygienic and dangerously ignorant, and there is no doubt that this stereotype did exist. However, others developed empirical skills that brought comfort and support to their neighbours. Flora Thompson fondly recalls "old Mrs Quinton" of Lark Rise "who, as she said, saw the beginning and end of everybody. ... She was a decent, intelligent old body, clean in her person and methods and very kind."[21]

Clearly, some of the folk remedies and herbal medicines preferred by 'old wives' were based more on superstition than on effective medication and were of dubious benefit. In 1890, Mrs Emma Dent of Sudeley Castle in Winchcombe collected and recorded local superstitions, "in order to preserve some of the quaint ideas and sayings which still linger in this corner of the Cotswolds". These included:

> For Whooping Cough - A roasted mouse to be eaten by the sufferer.
> The Ear Ache - A snail is procurred, and being pricked the exuded froth is dropped into the ear.
> For rheumatism - To carry a potato, or an onion, in the pocket.
> For consumption - To allow little frogs to jump down the throat.

When recording this final superstition, Mrs Dent "was solemnly assured by a labourer in a hay-field that he had been cured by this remedy. On asking him how he managed to persuade the little frogs to hop down his throat, he simply replied - 'by opening his mouth wide enough'." Walter Rose also recalls a resident of his Buckinghamshire village "who swallowed one live frog each spring, which, he held, maintained his health through the summer," whilst Rose himself ate live garden snails to ward off consumption. In Cambridgeshire, the same cures for whooping cough and rheumatism were practised as in Gloucestershire, but there ear ache was treated by placing the inner clove of an onion in the ear, whilst warts were cured by rubbing a slug on them. In Oxfordshire, Flora Thompson remembers "one old man, then nearly eighty, had for years drunk a tea-cupful of frothing soap-suds every Sunday morning. 'Them cleans the outers,' he would say, 'an' stands to reason they must clean th' innards, too.'" However, other remedies have subsequently been validated by science: raspberry leaf tea, recommended to help relieve labour pains and dysmenorrhoea, contains a uterine relaxant; nettles, described as 'good for the blood', contain Vitamin K; the application of mouldy dung to an open wound or sore may sound counter-productive, but the mould would have contained penicillin.[22]

Even the remedies proven to be beneficial were often accompanied by rituals: the 'old wife' of Gotherington in Gloucestershire believed in "the need of picking and collecting her herbs at particular times of the moon's phases, and considers each plant to be under the dominion of one of the planets". However, to dismiss such practices as mere superstition ignores the context in which 'old wives' practised. Even the ritual, as recorded by Emma Dent, that "after a corpse has been laid out, the window is opened to allow the spirit to pass out easily" gave solace and hope to the rural poor as part of an approach to health care which sought comfort and a sense of control as much in participation as in a solution.[23]

Lady Bountiful

In rural communities, the preparation and distribution of medicines to the sick poor had also been recognised as part of the traditional duties of 'Ladies Bountiful' since the Middle Ages. By the time Queen Victoria began her long reign in 1837, the cultural philosophy of domesticity had inextricably linked such charitable acts with what were seen as women's 'natural', virtuous traits. The fears and economic disruptions caused by the American and French Revolutions, and by the wars with France, combined with the revival of Evangelicalism, all produced an intense desire for order, stability and morality. This found expression in the definition of domesticity as the division of men's and women's worlds into public and private spheres. Contemporary thinkers such as Ruskin believed that it was the advanced, superior, nationalistic progress of this regulated society that had enabled women to be thus separated. Men - the educated, paternalistic guardians of society - grappled with the harsh realities of business and politics, whilst women devoted themselves to family, home and charitable good works. By spreading their values of morality, providence and self-discipline amongst the poor, middle and upper class women could act as agents of domesticity and, consequently, of social improvement.[24]

What the poor privately thought about Lady Bountiful's visits and ministrations is difficult to discern. In the Suffolk village of Helmingham, some of the villagers harboured an underlying, smouldering resentment: "'You were under and you dussn't say anything'", but others enjoyed "the cosy warmth of aristocratic contact". Flora Thompson recalls that many poor people "took a pride in their rich and powerful country-house neighbours, especially when titled". Clearly, the success of this altruism depended greatly on the personality of each individual Lady Bountiful, but in general her gifts were certainly regarded as less humiliating and degrading than parish relief, and in the light of the alternative forms of provision, at least offered a positive addition to rural health care.[25]

On the negative side, Lady Bountiful's sense of philanthropic duty could be used as a form of control in rural communities, demonstrating the dependence of the poor on their social superiors. Lucretia Cromwell, whose husband worked as a labourer for the Coatesworths, the main landowning family in the Cambridgeshire village of Gislea, remembers how "they used to give coats and blankets to the industrious poor. ... There was nothing else and if you didn't do what they wanted you to, what was the good if you got the sack?" The importance of such deference was further emphasised by the teacher's lessons and the vicar's sermons: a young girl who omitted to curtsey to Lady Tollemache in Helmingham, Suffolk, was caned at school next day; whilst Flora Thompson recalls that one of the favourite sermon subjects of the vicar at Lark Rise "was the supreme rightness of the social order as it then existed. God, in His infinite wisdom, had appointed a place for every man, woman, and child on this earth and it was their bounden duty to remain contentedly in their niches." Walter Rose also stresses how the influence of the weekly sermons at Haddenham cannot be over-estimated: "'The rich man in his castle, the poor man at the gate' were accepted as rightly ordained conditions."[26]

However, not all Ladies Bountiful felt the need to resort to coercion. Some sincerely regarded themselves as the natural guardians of the poor and custodians of their family's responsibility to the local community. Louise Jermy, who was born on the Broadlands estate in Hampshire in 1877, recalls, "The people reigning at Broadlands at that time were Lord and Lady Mount Temple, and ... they were adored by their tenantry." When Louise's mother and one-month-old brother both died, leaving her father a widower at the age of only twenty-three, with daughters of three and one-and-a-half years old, Lady Mount Temple paid the funeral expenses. In Winchcombe, at the official opening of the water supply in 1887, Emma Dent said to the assembled crowd:

> I hope you all believe what a really sincere pleasure it has always been to me and mine to take a part in anything relating to the good of Winchcombe ... and how it was the great wish of those who are gone to leave an influence for good ... among you. I seem to stand here today as their representative, and in their name, and to their memory.

When Mrs Dent died in 1900, the local Reverend, John Taylor, wrote: "To me it seems that the best and strongest influence which the neighbourhood knew has now departed. ... She cared for *individuals*. ... Her benefactions to the poor have flowed for years in a steady stream ... to remind you that you belonged to her big family." Women such as Lady Mount Temple and Mrs Dent knew the life history and circumstances of every family on their estate or within the neighbourhood and could readily identify those in need. Their altruistic character and attitude created warm bonds between rich and poor, which made acceptable the social system that their role was intended to support and sustain.[27]

Nevertheless, even the most well-intentioned ministrations could vary in quality and efficacy. Lady Wilbraham visited the cottages on her husband's estate in Cheshire every Saturday, armed with "a bottle of castor oil which was frequently administered, to the consternation of the recipients". Viscountess Milner recalled how, if cottagers were ill, her mother-in-law, Lady Salisbury, would mix together

> all the medicine bottles of her large family - all that were not actually marked 'poison' - would put the contents into bottles with an equal quantity of Lord Salisbury's best port wine, and would distribute these to the old women in the parish, who always declared that 'her ladyship's medicine did them more good than the Doctor's'.

Such examples may raise a wry smile and conjure up mental images of the cliche Lady Bountiful, ridiculed and caricatured by Dickens and *Punch*, yet at the same time they illustrate that, whilst some Ladies Bountiful were arrogant and autocratic with their tenants and employees, demonstrating insensitivity to the realities of working class life, many did feel a genuine altruistic concern for the poor.[28]

Towards the end of the nineteenth century, the more enlightened and insightful Ladies Bountiful, be they the wives and daughters of the aristocracy, the gentry or of clergymen, began to recognise that soup, home-made remedies and a gracious manner were not enough: what the sick poor needed was trained nursing care of the standard that society had come to expect from a reformed, skilled profession. Innovative individuals began to employ a nurse for their estate or surrounding villages, but whilst such initiatives were, doubtless, of great local value in remote rural areas, a focus and impetus were needed to create a national organisation to provide professional nursing care for the sick poor in their own homes. The necessary inspiration came not from a member of the aristocracy or the established rural gentry, but from a free-thinking, intellectual newcomer to country life: Elizabeth Malleson.

Notes

1. For example, see *Lancet,* 20 December 1879, p.919 and 11 December 1880, pp.946-7; *British Medical Journal*, 17 March 1880, p.996.
2. Christopher Maggs, 'Made, Not Born' in *Nursing Times*, Vol. 80 No. 38 (Sept 19-25, 1984), 31-34 (p.32).
   Lee Holcombe, *Victorian Ladies at Work*, (Newton Abbot: David & Charles, 1973), p.11.
   Stella Bingham, *Ministering Angels* (London: Osprey, 1979), p.105.
   Monica E. Baly, *Florence Nightingale and the Nursing Legacy* (London: Croom Helm, 1986), pp.190-1.
3. Rosemary White, *Social Change and the Development of the Nursing Profession* (London: Kimpton, 1978), pp.55, 59 & 61.
4. Gloucestershire Record Office (hereafter GRO) HO3 8/9 Cheltenham Hospital Annual Reports 1880-1889.
5. GRO D1070/VII/91 Fairford Cottage Hospital Annual Reports 1870-1923.
   GRO HO2 8/2 Bourton-on-the-Water Cottage Hospital Annual Reports 1875-1884.
6. GRO HO30 25/1 Reminiscences about foundation of Moreton-in-Marsh Cottage Hospital by Miss Rebecca Horne, the first Matron.
7. GRO D1070/VII/91.
8. GRO HO40 8/2 Tetbury Cottage Hospital Annual Reports 1871-91.
   GRO HO2 8/2.
9. Flora Thompson, *Lark Rise to Candleford* (Harmondsworth: Penguin, 1973 edition, first published 1939-43), p.90.
10. GRO G/WI/95/13 Winchcombe Union Workhouse Master's Journal 1880.
11. GRO G/SO/87 Chipping Sodbury Workhouse Punishment Books 1876-1947.
    GRO G/TEW/87 Tewkesbury Union Workhouse Punishment Books 1853-1929.
12. GRO G/STR/93 Stroud Union Workhouse Chaplain's Report Book 1847-91.
    GRO G/WI/95/13.
13. Ibid.
14. GRO G/TET/145/1 Tetbury District Medical Relief Book 1876-81.
    Pamela Horn, *Labouring Life in the Victorian Countryside* (Dublin: Gill & MacMillan, 1976), pp.184 & 193.
15. Ibid, pp.193-5.
16. Ibid, pp.183-4.
    Virginia Berridge, 'Health and Medicine', in *The Cambridge Social History of Britain 1750-1950: Vol. 3 Social Agencies and Institutions*, ed.

by F.M.L. Thompson (Cambridge University Press, 1990), pp.171-242 (pp.186-7).

17. *Lancet*, 1 April 1871, cited by Jean Towler & Joan Bramall, *Midwives in History and Society* (London: Croom Helm, 1986), pp.157-8.
18. Berridge, 'Health & Medicine', pp.181-2.
    GRO D2752 4/12 & 4/13 Walwins of Gloucester Prescription Books 1877-82.
    GRO D5792 Sellors of Tewkesbury Medical Recipes 1870-85.
    GRO D4457/1 Thompson of Tetbury Customers' Orders 1878-1904.
19. Berridge, 'Health & Medicine', p.191.
    Thompson, *Lark Rise*, p.136.
    Cheltenham Examiner, 14 January 1880, p.2, c.2.
    Angela Holdsworth, *Out of the Doll's House: The Story of Women in the Twentieth Century* (London: BBC Books, 1988), p.98.
20. Patricia Branca, *Silent Sisterhood: Middle-Class Women in the Victorian Home* (London: Croom Helm, 1975), p.67.
    Cheltenham Examiner, 14 January 1880, p.2, c.2.
21. Thompson, *Lark Rise*, p.135.
22. Horn, *Labouring Life*, p.187.
    Cheltenham Reference Library (hereafter CRL) 336G914 *The Winchcombe & Sudeley Record* 1890-96.
    Walter Rose, *Good Neighbours: Some Recollections of an English Village and its People* (Cambridge University Press, 1942), p.38.
    Mary Chamberlain, *Fenwomen: A Portrait of Women in an English Village* (London: Virago, 1975), p.184.
    Thompson, *Lark Rise*, pp.136-7.
    Mary Chamberlain, *Old Wives' Tales: Their History, Remedies and Spells* (London: Virago, 1981), p.177.
23. Lady Victoria Lambton & Mrs Elizabeth Malleson, 'Philanthropic Aspects of Nursing', in *Woman's Mission: A Series of Congress Papers on the Philanthropic Work of Women*, ed. by The Baroness Burdett-Coutts (London: Sampson Low, Marston, 1893), pp.206-215 (p.212).
    Chamberlain, *Old Wives'* Tales, p.3.
    CRL 336G914.
24. Leonore Davidoff & Catherine Hall, *Family Fortunes: Men & Women of the English Middle Class 1780-1850* (London: Century Hutchison, 1987), pp.358 & 115.
    Kate Millett, 'The Debate over Women: Ruskin vs Mill' in *Suffer & Be Still: Women in the Victorian Age*, ed. by Martha Vicinus (London: Methuen, 1972), pp.121-139.
    Anne Summers, 'A Home from Home: Women's Philanthropic Work in the Nineteenth Century' in *Fit Work for Women*, ed. by Sandra Burman (London: Croom Helm, 1979), pp.33-63, (p.59).

25. Jessica Gerard, 'Lady Bountiful: Women of the Landed Classes & Rural Philanthropy' in *Victorian Studies*, 30, Winter 1987, 183-210, (pp.92 & 200).
    George Ewart Evans, *Where Beards Wag All* (London: Faber & Faber, 1970), p.123.
    Thompson, *Lark Rise*, p.289.
26. Pamela Horn, *Ladies of the Manor: Wives & Daughters in Country-house Society 1830-1918* (Stroud: Sutton, 1991), p.113.
    Chamberlain, *Fenwomen*, pp.134-5.
    Gerard, 'Lady Bountiful', pp.201-2.
    Evans, *Beards*, p.122.
    Thompson, *Lark Rise*, pp.211-2.
    Rose, *Good Neighbours*, p.106.
27. Louise Jermy, *The Memories of a Working Woman* (Norwich: Goose, 1934), pp.1-7.
    CRL 336G914.
    CRL 336G283 *Winchcombe Parish Magazine*, April 1900.
    Gerard, 'Lady Bountiful', p.205.
    Horn, *Ladies of the Manor*, p.113.
28. Cited by Horn, *Ladies of the Manor*, pp.118-9 & 115.
    Gerard, 'Lady Bountiful', pp.200 & 205.

CHAPTER TWO
DISTRICT NURSING

The Village Nursing Association

According to the biography written by her youngest daughter, Hope, Elizabeth Malleson "had the qualities of the pioneer and leader ... and the indignant zeal of the reformer" at a time when 'strong-minded' was one of the most abusive terms that could be applied to a woman.[1] She was in her fifties before she became interested in nursing and it is valuable to consider briefly her early work, as this period of her life offers an insight into the motivation of a philanthropist of such tenacious determination.

Elizabeth was born in Chelsea in 1828, the eldest of the eleven children of Henry Whitehead, a Unitarian solicitor, and his wife Frances. The care and education of her younger siblings occupied Elizabeth at home until she was twenty-four years old. When she finally sought work, a brief period as a companion/secretary was followed by a post as a governess, then in 1854 she became a teacher at the progressive, non-denominational Portman Hall School established by Barbara Leigh-Smith.[2]

Elizabeth gave up teaching in 1857, when she married Frank Malleson, the son of a Unitarian minister, but education, particularly the education of women, remained a priority in her life. In 1864, she opened the College for Working Women in Bloomsbury, which offered evening classes in elementary reading, writing and arithmetic, as well as lectures in English literature, history, physiology and drawing. Elizabeth also campaigned strenuously for women's rights: she was a member of the Married Women's Property Committee, formed by Barbara Leigh-Smith in 1858; in 1864, she joined the Ladies London Emancipation Society; and in 1875 she supported John Stuart Mill's election to Parliament. Elizabeth actively took up the cause for the repeal of the Contagious Diseases Acts at a time when, as Hope Malleson expresses it, "friends looked askance at one another, workers in the cause were ostracized, and in public places skirts were drawn aside from contamination with people so shameless".[3]

The Mallesons lived in Wimbledon, with their three daughters and one son, and practised a generous and wholehearted hospitality. They went frequently into London society, attending monthly parties during the Season, and their large circle of energetic and influential friends included artists, writers, politicians, philanthropists and intellectuals. In particular, Elizabeth knew many of the Victorian women who dared to challenge the limited domestic role that society had assigned to them: the author George Eliot and the actress Ellen Terry were both her friends, and she also had contact with feminists and reformers such as Harriet Martineau, Octavia Hill, Elizabeth Garrett Anderson and Frances Power Cobbe. Elizabeth Malleson, as her daughter expresses it,

> lived in a stirring London world where new ideas and activities were quickly coming into being, and each new movement for social reform, especially where it concerned women, roused in her an immediate and eager response Her energy and vitality, her unfailing zest for life, [were] ever spurring her on to be up and doing in new fields of work for others.[4]

Her attitude of social responsibility reflected the views of late nineteenth century middle class campaigners who sought to harness overlapping, individual charities and co-ordinate philanthropic activities in urban areas. The work of groups such as the Charity Organisation Society brought system and order to previously sporadic alms-giving, and though their visitors were still volunteers and therefore unpaid, their application of social science techniques to the recording and judgement of each individual case introduced an element of professionalisation into customary philanthropic practices. However, in rural communities, the Ladies Bountiful were still a distinct group, with different motives to middle class lady visitors in the towns and cities. Their relationship with the poor, as we have seen, remained rooted in feudalism, staunchly conservative and, as Hope Malleson expresses it, "hardly stirred by the spirit of the time".[5]

This was the situation that awaited Elizabeth when, in 1881, her husband Frank decided to retire from his business as a wine merchant in London and move to the country. The following year, the Mallesons moved to sixteenth-century Dixton Manor House in the heart of the Cotswolds. In the Gloucestershire countryside, in stark contrast to her busy Wimbledon lifestyle, Elizabeth found herself with no neighbours within a mile, whilst the post office was five miles away at Winchcombe, and shops and the railway station were seven miles away in Cheltenham. Whilst Frank happily immersed himself in the management of farm animals and breeding horses, Elizabeth, with characteristic vigour, looked for a new cause to champion. She turned the inquiring eyes of a newcomer to well-established and long-accepted local problems and quickly became aware of the living conditions of her poorer neighbours, though her initial involvement with the local cottagers concerned not their health problems but leisure facilities.[6]

The road to Cheltenham took the Mallesons through the village of Gotherington, which suffered isolation and neglect from having an absentee landlord, who lived four miles away at 'Rosehill', Pittville, and no resident minister, the parish church and rector being two miles away at Bishops Cleeve. Contemporary documents describe Gotherington as including "various-sized agricultural holdings, each with good farm house and ample homestead attached, several excellent small holdings ... and a number of cottages". The 1881 census records a population of 388, of whom eight men described themselves as "domestic gardeners" (presumably market gardeners). Local maps show that there were 46 orchards which would have provided grazing for animals, fruit for the Cheltenham market, and apples and pears for the local cider mills. In the 1891 census, tenant farmers and farm labourers represented 70% of men aged between 15 and 65; another 9% were village craftsmen - blacksmiths, carpenters and wheelwrights, shoemakers and stonemasons. The small cottages in the village, occupied by the agricultural labourers, were mostly built of stone with thatched roofs; a few were brick-built with slate roofs and stone floors which were cold and damp in winter. Most of the cottages had a garden and often a pigsty. If the cottages were semi-detached, the outside closet was sometimes shared. Some cottagers had piped water supplied from a private reservoir at one of the farms, for which they paid an annual rate of five shillings, but many depended on wells or pumps.[7]

As Hope recalls, Elizabeth saw that, in the cottages, "the one tiny kitchen/sitting-room, the only one with a fire in it, was always fully occupied by the younger children, the frequent baby and the toiling mother who, of necessity, carried on all her household tasks in it. It provided the father and sons home from work with little beyond a fruitful cause of discord." What was needed, Elizabeth decided, "was a common room ... where the men and elder boys could pass some of their hours of leisure in the long winter afternoons and evenings, and where they could find warmth and light and amusement other than that provided by the public house." [8]

Unfortunately, James Hutchinson, the absentee landlord, disapproved of a Reading Room in the village. Hutchinson, a traditional Tory, did not believe that the Liberal Mallesons either could or would run the club on non-political lines, and he also feared that if he supported the club and it failed, he would be held liable for its debts. However, Elizabeth was undaunted by Hutchinson's disapproval. Within a year, she found a suitable room to rent in one of the larger houses in the village; willing volunteers were organised to decorate it; gifts of furniture and books were sought from friends; and funds were raised by donations, bazaars and jumble sales. For a subscription of one penny a week, the men and boys over fourteen years of age could read books and newspapers, and play bagatelle, draughts, dominoes or cards. The room was also open in the afternoons, when the women and girls were encouraged to read and to attend classes in knitting and cookery. The Reading Room was managed on strictly democratic principles, with both men and women sitting on the committee of elected members with Elizabeth, her husband and their daughters. The Mallesons also opened their own home to the villagers: "Dances were occasionally given at Dixton to members of the reading-room and their friends, and a yearly entertainment in the Christmas holidays with tea, supper and theatricals became an institution." [9]

It was this close contact with the villagers of Gotherington which brought to Elizabeth's attention the urgent need of skilled nursing in such remote rural areas, especially for women in childbirth. The local women who acted as untrained midwives and nurses in Gotherington and its neighbouring villages personified the negative stereotype as discussed in Chapter One. They were, Hope tells us, "too often rough, ignorant women given to drink, who supplemented their earnings by charring or hauling coals or working in the fields", whilst the local 'wise woman' was described by Elizabeth as an "aged crone ... truly a relic of heathen superstition!" [10]

Elizabeth did acknowledge that "there is no lack of kindness and good-nature" amongst country people, but she deplored "the willingness of the neighbours to attend the sick ... with the audacity of ignorance ... where trained skill and sound knowledge are urgently required". In particular, she shuddered to recall "the nasty compounds which are applied as poultices ... some of them too bad to describe to ears polite", a reference, no doubt, to the rural tradition, certainly not unique to Gloucestershire, of applying a mouldy cow-pat to an infected wound (see Chapter One). Invalids were confined either to an unventilated bedroom with the window permanently closed and the chimney boarded up; or to the draughty passage between the front and back doors, which often caused bronchitis and other secondary chest infections. In cases of infectious diseases, the villagers' attitude was often one of the greatest obstacles to overcome: "The people appear to be fatalists on this subject, and regard the most ordinary prudence as flying in the face of Providence - their argument being, 'If you are to have it, you will have it,' and they go about the surest way to take, and spread, whatever the infection may be." Elizabeth also lamented the cottagers' ignorance of nutrition. From just a few weeks of age, babies were fed on "biscuit soaked in water ... cabbage and brown sugar, and fat bacon to suck", whilst at three or four months old, "a little of anything the elders are having is thought in many families good for the baby". Nor had the cottagers any knowledge of hygiene and sanitation: "An open stagnant ditch, or drain, is considered quite a suitable playground for the children, and to throw all refuse just outside the door is still a common practice." [11]

To combat these problems, Elizabeth resolved to raise sufficient funds to train a nurse for the village. To this end, she wrote to the local Liberal newspaper, the *Cheltenham Examiner*, in November 1883, appealing for donations. She also produced a Preliminary Prospectus, handwritten copies of which were sent to influential local people for their approval and subscriptions. Once she had gathered sufficient local support, a printed version was circulated to a larger, national circle of potential sponsors. In the printed prospectus, dated 1884, Elizabeth stresses the dangers of

> the services of untrained midwives who, guided by experience only, are not fitted to discriminate between normal and abnormal cases, and are equally unfit to restore their patients to health, or to take the initiative care of the infants. ... It is hardly necessary to point out the extreme suffering, and the risks to health and life which exist under this state of things.

In cases of illness or accidents, "in village homes there is not even elementary knowledge of what should be done, and a Nurse is urgently needed both to advise, and assist, in the mitigation of suffering and the restoration to health". As well as offering care, "a kindly Nurse living amongst cottagers would also become a valuable influence in the spread and observance of sanitary knowledge".[12]

The appeal raised £21.12s.6d. and enabled Elizabeth to found what she initially called the Village Nursing Association, with herself as Honorary Secretary. The list of those approving the scheme included London-based doctors, such as Elizabeth Garrett Anderson; matrons, including Eva Luckes of the London Hospital; nurses, such as Florence Dacre Craven and Rosalind Paget; and Louisa Twining, the Poor Law Guardian for Kensington. Two local doctors, Mr William Cox of Winchcombe and Mr D. Devereux, the Surgeon of Tewkesbury Hospital, also approved of the scheme, the former acting as Treasurer of the Association. However, whilst Elizabeth acknowledged that their "cordial support ... is nominally given me freely", she added that "they are hard-worked men who have small enthusiasm for reforms".[13]

Nevertheless, Elizabeth herself remained enthusiastic. Her original plan was to select a suitable local woman and send her to Queen Charlotte's Hospital in London to train, so she could then return to the village to live and work amongst her friends and neighbours. However, "an entirely suitable person seemed impossible to find within a limited area". It was then decided to appoint a woman from outside the district who was already trained and who "might get employment ... with patients who could pay fees into the Fund, according to a fixed scale, and so help her own maintenance for poorer women". As Elizabeth continues in her *Trained Midwife & Village Nurse Report* dated March 1886:

> After careful searching a suitable woman was found, accustomed to country life, and already trained both as Midwife and sick nurse. She came to Gotherington early in September 1885. ... Some waiting was of course to be expected while the village women got to know her, and to trust her. But Nurse Mary turned this time to good account. ... Neither fatigue, distance, nor bad weather daunted her; she has attended patients in and around Cleeve, Woodmancote, Prescott, Stanway, and has proved herself most kindly, energetic, devoted, and suited to her position.

During November 1885, Nurse Mary "paid ninety-six visits to the invalids on her list", as well as attending midwifery cases. Not "content to visit her patients during the day ... she has taken up her abode in the cottages, and devoted herself to her patients' welfare, looking after the house and tending the children". As a result of her care, mothers had been able to remain in bed until after the ninth or tenth post-natal day and had "recovered and resumed their household labours" in an "excellent state".[14]

Elizabeth pronounced the experiment a "full success" and appealed for further donations to continue the work, for "what the women can afford to pay cannot possibly maintain nursing of this kind". The original fund had only increased to £33.12s.0d., of which £28 had been paid to Nurse Mary in weekly wages of £1. Elizabeth was anxious that the experiment should not "fall to the ground" and she stressed that donating to the fund offered subscribers "a means of service which, quite unostentatiously, helps their poorer neighbours in times of sickness and trial, when skill, care and kindness avert serious dangers to health and life, and ensure much good result".[15]

Unfortunately, the response was disappointing; after nine months, the funds were exhausted and the experiment ended. However, national events were beginning to raise public awareness of the need for district nurses.

Queen Victoria's Jubilee Institute for Nurses

In 1887, as part of the celebrations for Queen Victoria's Golden Jubilee, the women of England were invited to make donations to a Jubilee Fund. Three million women between them subscribed £82,000, and after personal gifts of jewellery had been designed and executed by Carringtons of Regent Street, and a statue of Prince Albert had been commissioned for Windsor Park, the Queen was asked to decide how the remaining £70,000 should be spent. From various plans submitted to her, Queen Victoria chose a scheme produced by Florence Nightingale and William Rathbone to provide professionally trained and supervised nurses for the sick poor in their own homes.

William Rathbone (1819-1902), a philanthropic merchant, had already set up a highly organised and successful district nursing scheme in his home town of Liverpool in the 1860s, following the death of his first wife from consumption in 1859. Rathbone had been deeply impressed by the comfort and care his wife had received from a private nurse, Mary Robinson, and he was determined that the sick poor should have access to the same standard of home nursing as the middle and upper classes. To this end, he asked Robinson to work amongst the poor of Liverpool for three months, not only as a nurse, but also as a moral agent. Robinson was overwhelmed by the misery and hopelessness she encountered and after one month she told Rathbone that she found it impossible to continue. He persuaded her to complete the three month trial period and gradually her efforts began to take effect. Inspired by the success of this initial experiment, Rathbone resolved to extend the scheme, at his own expense, and in 1861 he wrote to Florence Nightingale asking for her advice and support.

A voluminous correspondence followed, in which Nightingale suggested that the only way to ensure an adequate supply of suitable nurses was to set up a special training school at the Liverpool Royal Infirmary, where Rathbone was a member of the management committee. In 1862, the Liverpool Training School & Home for Nurses was duly opened, under the superintendence of Miss Merryweather who had trained at the Nightingale School at St Thomas' Hospital in London. Thus the precedent was set that district nurses should be hospital trained, preferably under the Nightingale reformed system, before being specially trained in district work. By 1867, the city of Liverpool had been divided into eighteen districts, each with its own nurse and each organised by a philanthropic lady volunteer and lay committee.

The success of the Liverpool system proved a stimulus to other large towns and cities. Manchester and Birmingham each founded a similar scheme, but in London only sparse care was offered by organisations such as the East London Nursing Society and the Ranyard Bible Nurses, both formed in 1868. In 1874, the Duke of Westminster and Sir Edmund Lechmere of the English branch of the Order of St John of Jerusalem wrote to Rathbone proposing that a system of district nursing be set up in London. Rathbone was, by then, a Liberal MP and consequently spent part of each year in the capital, thus enabling him to offer both help and support for the London scheme. He immediately wrote to Nightingale, suggesting that they should take advantage "of the interest now excited to try to get for London a scheme for organising the disjointed efforts in the metropolis into our plan."[16] At that time, Nightingale was at her family home in Derbyshire. Her father had died in January 1874 and she had temporarily returned to care for her mother, who was eighty-six, frail and confused. Nightingale was, therefore, unable to personally organise the London scheme, but, as with the Liverpool system, she did everything that she could from a distance. She wrote a pamphlet, *Suggestions for Improving the Nursing Service for the Sick Poor*, and she selected Miss Florence Lees to carry out a detailed survey on the existing provision and district nursing needs in London.

Florence Sarah Lees (later Mrs Dacre Craven) was born in 1841 and grew up in comfortable circumstances in St Leonards, Sussex. In 1866, she trained at the Nightingale School at St Thomas' Hospital, then travelled throughout Europe, nursing and visiting hospitals in Germany, France, Holland, Belgium, Denmark, Austria and Italy. During the Franco-Prussian War (1870-1), at the request of the Crown Princess Frederick (the eldest daughter of Queen Victoria), and on the recommendation of Florence Nightingale, Lees organised the nursing in a military hospital in Prussia. In recognition of her war service, Lees became the first woman ever to receive the Prussian Order of the Iron Cross. In 1873, she visited hospitals in the USA and Canada, on her return to England, Lees agreed to undertake the nursing survey. She subsequently produced a meticulous report which showed that, at that time, there were only 106 district nurses for the whole of London. Many of these nurses, employed by a total of twenty-two religious and philanthropic organisations, were only partially trained or had no training at all.

As a result of the report, the Metropolitan Nursing Association (MNA) was formed in 1875, with Lees as Superintendent General. She was responsible for recruiting and supervising the trainees who, after completing the standard one year's training as Lady Probationers at the Nightingale School, were trained specifically as district nurses. The Central Home at 23 Bloomsbury Square provided comfortable accommodation for five nurses, who paid for their training, with an emphasis on discipline, both on and off duty. The trainees worked an eight-hour day, six hours in their district with the other two hours devoted to lectures or reading. They were allowed two hours leisure time in the evening and were guaranteed eight hours sleep a night. This rigorous training, which combined personal devotion with technical excellence, reflected Nightingale's belief, expressed in a letter to *The Times* in April 1876, that to fulfil the gruelling and responsible duties involved in caring for the sick poor in their own homes,

> A district nurse ... must be of a yet higher class and of a yet fuller training than a hospital nurse, because she has not the doctor always at hand; because she has no hospital appliances at hand at all; and because she has to take notes of the case for the doctor, who has no one but her to report to him. She is his staff of clinical clerks, dressers, and nurses.[17]

In response, *The Lancet* criticised her ideas as "somewhat rambling and incoherent precepts" expressed in a style which "sadly lacks conciseness and clearness". They expressed the opinion that district nurses would be better employed by "the class who have some education, but who for the most part perform their own domestic work and keep no servants", such as clerks and warehousemen, for whom "the acceptance of help should not involve any loss of self-respect". The poor, on the other hand, "resent the intrusion of strangers" and if "a district nurse spies out the filthiness of a home, and makes a report which brings down inspectors ... [she] is likely to become a most unpopular personage". They questioned the efficacy of encouraging the poor to remain in "unwholesome dwellings" during sickness when they could be removed to a hospital, and they suggested that the £20,000 which Nightingale hoped to raise for her scheme would be better spent building "a hospital of one hundred beds" or improved housing for the poor than providing "women who, in spite of training and an ability to take temperatures and scientific notes, might not always be a welcome addition to a small household".[18]

However, *The Lancet* had always been critical of Nightingale's theories, particularly her belief that nurses should be educated ladies who could influence the behaviour of the working classes through the power of social example, as well as caring for them. The very purpose of district nursing, in Nightingale's opinion, was to separate the sick poor from each other rather than grouping them together in hospitals, and it appears that the public, the media, and the majority of the medical profession in London did not support *The Lancet* 's contrary view. When Nightingale's letter to *The Times* was reprinted as a pamphlet, *On Trained Nursing for the Sick Poor*, it ran to two editions, and doctors in working class areas acknowledged the value of the nurses' services.

The last quarter of the nineteenth century was in general a period of political and social reform. A plethora of wide-ranging legislation was passed in response to the growing awareness that the material conditions of the poor were as essential a part of paternalism as salvation of the soul.

This combination of social and religious motives was manifest in the growing numbers and variety of urban visiting societies, whose volunteers could be found in hospitals, workhouses, prisons and asylums, as well as in the homes of the poor. In this context of national reform, the establishment and success of the MNA can be seen as reflecting the recognised need to improve the lives of the poor, and by 1886 seven branches had been formed in various parts of London. Its work was confined to the capital, but Nightingale predicted that "within a few years ... [it] will be a disgrace ... to any district ... not to have a good District Nurse to nurse the sick poor at home".[19]

When suggestions were invited for the use of the Women's Jubilee Offering, Nightingale and her supporters saw the opportunity not only to place the MNA on a solid financial footing, but also to extend its work throughout England. William Rathbone prepared a draft plan, which was then sent to Nightingale for her comments and input, particularly concerning the selection and training of district nurses. When the final plan was submitted for the Queen's consideration, it was chosen in preference to several other suggestions, such as supporting emigration. Queen Victoria was known to be sympathetic to nursing and she had followed Nightingale's career with interest. After the Crimean War, Her Majesty had entertained her at Balmoral, where Prince Albert had been impressed by her intelligence and modesty. The Queen herself was said to be "enchanted with her" and in 1861 had offered her a 'grace and favour' apartment in Kensington Palace, which had been refused.[20] Vicky, the Crown Princess of Prussia, had maintained a correspondence with Florence Lees after the Franco-Prussian War. Following Lees' marriage to the Reverend Dacre Craven in 1878 and the subsequent birth of their eldest son, Vicky had become the child's godmother. In addition, the Duke of Westminster, as well as being Chairman of the MNA, was also Chairman of the Jubilee Fund. These links were, without doubt, important in influencing the Queen's choice of how the Jubilee Fund should be spent, but nursing historian Monica Baly believes that the establishment of a national district nursing scheme was also made possible at this time by "the changing social scene, the new awareness of the health needs of the community, together with the greater emancipation and better education of women at the end of the century".[21] To this could be added the reform and professionalisation both of nursing itself and of philanthropy. These factors all combined to create a climate of collective endeavour in which a perceived need was translated into action with the support of royal patronage.

However, when the Court Circular in *The Times* announced the Queen's choice, the reaction was not wholly favourable. The announcement itself was brief and vague: "The Queen has decided that the surplus of the Women's Jubilee Offering shall be devoted to the benefit of nurses or nursing establishments, and has requested a committee to advise her on the best mode of giving effect to this intention." In its 'Leader' that day, *The Times* made two questionable assumptions, firstly that "as the fund was contributed by women, it will be by women that the benefit from it will be felt ... [by the] provision for the nursing of sick women and girls", and secondly that the advisory committee would be "a committee of gentlemen". Neither statement reflected the Nightingale/Rathbone plan, but both reflected the traditional view of the running of a philanthropic society as comparable to the running of a patriarchal family: men were to provide the intelligence and direction, and women would benefit from their superior benevolence and guidance.[22]

That the fund should be handed back to the nation at all gave rise to objection, as expressed by 'Two County Collectors': "The collection would hardly have been taken up with so much enthusiasm in all parts of the kingdom had we not all felt it as an act of personal devotion to our beloved Queen, and it would be a cause for regret should the offering be divested of this personal element." The personal gift of jewellery to the Queen was only commissioned after the Countess of Strafford, President of the Women's Jubilee Offering, suggested that the great majority of subscribers desired "that Her Majesty would allow a small portion of the sum to be devoted to a memento of her jubilee which would be both personal and lasting".[23]

On the other hand, one correspondent believed that "the great multiplication of district nurses and district nursing institutions under the auspices of the Queen's jubilee will prove an untold blessing to thousands upon thousands of the sick and poor throughout the country", whilst 'A Loyal Collector' in a small country parish "frequently heard a hope expressed by the poor that such a thing might be thought of".[24]

On 20th September 1889, a Royal Charter was issued, formally establishing Queen Victoria's Jubilee Institute for Nurses (QVJI). The first Council of 22 members, selected by the Queen herself, included the Duke of Westminster, William Rathbone, Florence Nightingale's cousin Henry Bonham Carter, and the Reverend and Mrs Craven (formerly Miss Lees), all of whom were known supporters of Nightingale and her methods. The degree of royal approval and involvement in district nursing was further reflected by the inclusion on the Council of all three of Her Majesty's own daughters who were still resident in Britain at that time, Their Royal Highnesses the Princesses Christian, Louise and Beatrice.

This Queen's Council accepted the MNA as the model for the new QVJI. Its training and syllabus were adopted, as was its most important and innovatory precept that its nurses should be supervised not by religious bodies or by a philanthropic laity who knew little or nothing of nursing, but by local Superintendents and national Inspectors who were themselves both educated ladies and highly trained nurses. To this end, the Council's first task was to appoint an Inspector General and for this exacting and important role they selected Miss Rosalind Paget, a niece of William Rathbone.

Paget had trained as a nurse at the London Hospital and as a midwife at the London Lying-in Hospital; she had nursing experience at hospitals in Liverpool, Manchester and London. At the age of thirty-four, she accepted the post of QVJI's first Inspector General. As she wanted to be seen as a professional nurse, not an amateur Lady Bountiful, she accepted a salary of £100 a year, but she gave the wage back to the Institute. For the same reason, she also insisted on completing three months training as a district nurse with the MNA before taking up her post. As Inspector General of QVJI, Paget was responsible for all matters relating to the training of nurses, including the setting up of schools of district nursing. Existing urban district nursing associations, which conformed to the general principles of the foundation, were invited to apply for affiliation with QVJI, and it was part of Paget's duties to make the often delicate and difficult decision of acceptance or rejection. Not surprisingly, one of the first to apply and be accepted was William Rathbone's own scheme in Liverpool, whose pioneering work in the 1860s had now, he said, spread "far beyond anything that even the most sanguine of us could then foresee".[25]

The Rural Nursing Association

As the detailed plans for QVJI progressed, Elizabeth Malleson persisted with her efforts to provide village nurse/midwives, this time on a national scale. Locally, her short-lived experience with the Village Nursing Association had certainly not been unique: in the Christchurch area of Cheltenham, the Reverend Fenn had established a system of district nursing as early as 1867 but it had closed in 1872 due to lack of funds; and in Charlton Kings a Parish Nurse had been engaged in 1883 but, again, insufficient monies caused the scheme to be abandoned at Easter 1885. Nationally, small, independent rural nursing schemes had been successfully set up by philanthropic individuals, but they were scattered all over England, and as Hope Malleson tells us, "E.M. realised how much more could be accomplished by co-operation, by the existence of a central body which could set and maintain the standard of nursing, and which could ask for funds to help poor districts and to train suitable women."

Elizabeth again used the method of circulating the Village Nursing Association prospectus to potential supporters, then reprinting it "headed by the names of eminent doctors and women well known in the nursing profession who approved of her scheme. Among the latter was the name of Florence Nightingale."[26]

Hope's mention of Florence Nightingale in a separate short sentence emphasises the importance she, and Elizabeth Malleson herself, attached to Nightingale's support. However, Hope seems to have chosen to embellish the truth, as Florence Nightingale's name does not, in fact, appear on the prospectus. In June 1888, Elizabeth did write to Nightingale, asking for her support. Unfortunately, Nightingale's reply does not appear to have survived, but it is clear from a second letter which Elizabeth sent her, in July 1888, that, in fact, she refused to lend her name to the scheme. Although Nightingale's letter is missing, it is possible to deduce what were the main points of her reply, by considering other letters which she wrote about district nursing and by examining Elizabeth's two letters to her. When William Rathbone had sought Nightingale's advice and support for his Liverpool scheme, she wrote to him in November 1861: "Your plans ... have deeply interested me from the very first: they appeared to me so well considered and laid out - they appeared to me so much needed, not only in Liverpool, but in all the earth ... [and] promise extensive and invaluable good ... which will spread to every town and district in the kingdom." In June 1867, she wrote to her cousin Henry Bonham Carter, who, as noted earlier, became a member of the first Queen's Council of QVJI: "My view you know is that the ultimate destination of all nursing is the nursing of the sick in their own homes. ... I look to the abolition of all hospitals and workhouse infirmaries. But it is no use to talk about the year 2000." Furthermore, what is probably her most famous book, *Notes on Nursing,* which was first published in 1859, is mainly concerned not with hospital nursing, but with nursing in the home.[27]

It is clear from such sources and, of course, from her involvement with the MNA and the plan on which QVJI was based, that Florence Nightingale thoroughly approved of district nursing. Therefore, the reason for her rejection of Elizabeth Malleson's plan must lie in Elizabeth's approach to her. Hope Malleson describes her mother as "courageously unconventional. ... No one could have been less affected than she by what others said or thought once she was sure of her ground. And always her actions were very direct. Subtlety and finesse had no place in them." Consequently, she did not approach Florence Nightingale through the medium of a mutual acquaintance, or with a letter of introduction or testimonial, as the accepted rules of etiquette would suggest. She simply wrote to her direct, albeit in reverential tones:

Madam,

I trust you will be good enough to read the accompanying prospectus as it states briefly why I, a stranger, venture to trouble you. The subject of the paper has forced itself upon my attention ever since I came into Gloucestershire 5 or 6 years ago, and touches nearly, interests to which you have devoted your life.

I apply to you in the hope that if you recognise the evils which I have endeavoured to represent, you may allow your honoured name to be placed at the head of the Association I hope to form.

I believe the magic of its influence would do more to help the cause for which I plead than anything else.

Elizabeth enclosed with her letter a slightly reworded, handwritten copy of the 1884 Preliminary Prospectus of the Village Nursing Association. This document does set out very effectively the need for trained nurses in rural areas, but it gives no real indication of how the Association would be organised and run on a national scale. It merely suggests that the scheme should "be tried in two or three groups of villages in Gloucestershire". Florence Nightingale always stressed the importance of detail and meticulous planning, and all the features that most impressed her in William Rathbone's plans for his Liverpool scheme are missing from Elizabeth Malleson's prospectus.[28]

In addition, Elizabeth did not enclose the list of those who already approved of the scheme, even though they included Florence Dacre Craven, Rosalind Paget and Walter Pye, Surgeon to St Mary's Hospital who also lectured to the MNA. Therefore, Florence Nightingale had no indication of how much support Elizabeth Malleson had already raised. Indeed, the nearest she offers to any form of a character reference in her letter is to say, "there may be yet some friend of the late Miss Julia Smith" who could vouch for her. Elizabeth was, no doubt, wise not to mention her close friendship with Nightingale's illegitimate cousin Barbara Leigh Smith, but claiming the acquaintance of their mutual aunt was hardly the best of recommendations. As a young woman, Cecil Woodham-Smith tells us in her definitive biography of Nightingale, Julia Smith had "held 'advanced' views and suffered from nerves". She was so temperamental that Nightingale, as a child, "had christened her 'the stormy Ju'", and "in her old age Aunt Julia ... was subject to fits of hysterical depression during which she wept for hours on end". It is, therefore, highly doubtful that Nightingale was impressed by Elizabeth's friendship with her youngest maternal aunt.[29]

Nor did Elizabeth give Nightingale any indication of the many and varied charitable works with which she had been involved during the years when she lived at Wimbledon, and the organisational skills that these had involved. She declares unequivocally: "I do not lightly or foolishly engage in enterprise I cannot be trusted to carry out", but unfortunately she then counters her own claim to infallibility by ending the letter: "If I fail to get the influential, local and other support needed to form the Association, I would acquaint you without loss of time, in order to preserve your name being in any way linked with a failure."[30]

It is clear from Elizabeth's second letter, dated 17th July 1888, that Florence Nightingale did reply to the first letter, in detail, questioning Elizabeth's credentials for setting up and running a national nursing association, whether it could be run from a remote rural area of Gloucestershire, how sufficient funds would be raised, and where and how suitable nurse/midwives would be recruited. The July letter covers nine pages, and whilst it begins in a tone of reverence and gratitude, it gradually changes to one of argument and criticism:

> I cannot thank you adequately for the sympathetic kindness of your letter of July 7th and for the trouble you have taken to send me valuable notes for my encouragement and guidance. ...
>
> Your words as to the necessity of increasing the means of midwifery training before compelling 'registration on impossible conditions' have so much weight coming from you. ...
>
> I may cling perhaps too tenaciously to my mode of solving the difficulty. ... I am willing to concede that, living at this distance from London, I am not the proper person to initiate a 'Central Association', but my hope was that if I could collect a body of influential names to testify to the extreme need of trained midwifery and sick nursing in villages, I should be able so to rouse local opinion around me, as to be able to start a scheme, which if successful, might be followed in other parts of the country. ...
>
> I value so highly all you have kindly put before me that without commenting upon points where your wisdom confirms my own observation, I have answered in order others of your notes. ...

If Elizabeth hoped to further her own cause and to change Nightingale's mind, her subsequent comments defeated her aim. In particular, in reply to Nightingale's suggestion that she could employ a district nurse already trained by the MNA, Elizabeth questioned her most fundamental belief that nurses should be educated ladies:

In this neighbourhood I am inclined to think the work is more fitted to some of the excellent women I have known as nurses, than to ladies. The inevitable daily walking is a great trial of strength ... and the necessary spending of whole nights in cottages would seem a little more endurable to women less fastidious than the most sensitive.

When it is remembered that Elizabeth's nursing experience at that time consisted of a mere nine months experiment with one nurse, albeit a successful trial, and that is compared with the knowledge and expertise of the lady to whom she was writing, then her approach can hardly be described as tactful. There is no evidence of any further correspondence between them, so it is doubtful that Nightingale replied to Elizabeth's second letter.[31]

Why Hope Malleson chose to state so emphatically that Nightingale supported the Rural Nursing Association is a matter of speculation. It is, of course, feasible that, writing almost forty years after the event, Hope remembered that her mother had corresponded with Florence Nightingale and she assumed that the approach must have been successful. However, the early papers relating to the Rural Nursing Association were so carefully and proudly preserved by Elizabeth's family that it seems unlikely that Hope did not have access to them when she wrote her mother's biography. It appears more probable that, in view of the fact that Florence Nightingale's Metropolitan Nursing Association and Elizabeth Malleson's Rural Nursing Association were both later absorbed into QVJI, Hope chose, with more tact than her mother possessed, to omit their initial disagreement and to present them as like-minded women, both working for the good of the sick poor, rather than admit that the indomitable Elizabeth failed to secure Florence Nightingale's support for her rural scheme.

Nevertheless, Elizabeth Malleson persevered with her plan, even though Florence Nightingale was not her only critic. Both locally and nationally,

she encountered opposition from many quarters - from the medical profession, from country residents whose deeply-rooted conviction was that things were quite right as they were since they had sufficed for countless previous generations, from the villagers themselves who were shy of any change. ... For a long period E.M. seemed to be battling alone against an inert mass of prejudice.

However, as with her encounters with the local landowner, James Hutchinson, and with Florence Nightingale, Elizabeth's own attitude and approach needs to be considered as a contributory factor. Hope admits that her mother "had a dominating personality. ... Some found her formidable ... too strong in her convictions. ... [She] took swift dislikes and personal prejudices, and she had a way of expressing these and her displeasure and indignation in vehement tones ... startling to an offender". In their country life, the Mallesons developed a small, inner circle of friends, but Elizabeth found the social claims of neighbours and acquaintances, including garden parties and other local entertainments, "a sore infliction". After the stimulating, intellectual company of her forward-thinking London friends, Elizabeth found the society of country parsons and county gentry a necessity to be endured, rather than enjoyed, for the furtherance of her work amongst the poor:

> She paid the absolutely necessary duty calls ... [and] with incurable optimism she held that even with the dullest a subject of mutual interest could be discovered. But with her scorn of small talk and as she would not listen to gossip, conversation had to be at a certain level or languish. Often ... she returned openly lamenting the wasted time and her own fruitless efforts.

She must have been a difficult visitor to entertain and it is possible that comments such as, "Children have been born for generations under these conditions (around us). Why should I, or anyone trouble about it?" may have been, at least in part, a reaction to Elizabeth herself, rather than as she ascribes it to "a callous indifference ... [to] what I have been endeavouring to do for the last 5 or 6 years, with a heart wrung by the needs and abuses I have been forced to see".[32]

Elizabeth herself was undoubtedly middle class and an accepted member of the London intelligentsia, but it is, perhaps, not difficult to appreciate how her unorthodox views and forthright approach offended the traditional rural gentry and aristocracy, who frowned upon her as an interloper "interfering unwarrantably with the established order of things". Characteristically, Elizabeth resolved that "if she 'could not work with'" her neighbours, "she would 'fight them'". Through a combination of persuasion, argument and determination, "the cold shoulder gave way gradually to reluctant approval" and by 1889 she had formed "a small committee of sympathizers ... on the borders of Gloucestershire and Worcestershire". Active support was also offered on a national level by Lady Victoria Lambton of Pembrokeshire, the Countess of Selborne representing Hampshire and the Hon Mrs John Dundas of Yorkshire.[33]

In September 1889, Mrs Dundas wrote a letter to *The Times* in which she reiterated the text of the Preliminary Prospectus and suggested that the problem of raising sufficient funds to cover annual expenses could be solved

> if higher class women, possessed of some little means of their own, would take up village nursing as a distinct vocation, working under the auspices and encouragement of ladies of good position, who would visit them on equal terms, and thus obviate the objections of friends who might otherwise fear their losing caste by undertaking such work.[34]

In response, *The Nursing Record*, whilst acknowledging that the scheme was "excellent in theory", was inclined to believe that "to succeed in village Nursing, the Nurse, ... above all, must be drawn from the people amongst whom she is to work", and unless such nurses were "also willing to live amongst the villagers as one of themselves, they will not succeed". Their comments prompted an immediate response from Elizabeth Malleson, who leapt to the defence of Mrs Dundas. In complete contradiction of her emphatic criticism of Florence Nightingale's views the previous year, she now asserted that

> I do not agree that a Trained Midwife 'must be drawn from the people amongst whom she is to work'. Besides training, women who are Nurses should have (as I am sure you will agree) valuable mental and moral qualities, which it is by no means easy to find in one person, and it is certainly not common to find the possessors of these qualities in every village or group of villages where nursing services are needed.[35]

Despite Elizabeth's dominating personality and supreme confidence, Hope Malleson insists that "she was not only free of conceit but ... her potent influence did not lead her into that pitfall of the strong - love of power for its own sake". From her defence of Mrs Dundas, it appears that she was, at least, prepared to revise her views, in the light of her own growing experience and to accommodate the knowledge and opinions of other workers, as her scheme progressed and expanded.[36]

Among the experienced local members of the committee, Elizabeth Malleson was fortunate to have gained the support of Lady Lucy Hicks-Beach, who lived near Cirencester. With her husband, Sir Michael Hicks-Beach, later the Earl of St Aldwyn, Lady Lucy had, for some years, been actively involved in the administration of their local Cottage Hospital at Fairford. Sir Michael had been a Tory cabinet minister since the days of Disraeli's leadership, serving variously as Irish Secretary, Colonial

Secretary, President of the Board of Trade and Chancellor of the Exchequer.

On 14th May 1890, a meeting was held at 11 Downing Street, at Lady Lucy's invitation, to consider "the employment of Trained Midwives and Nurses in country districts". Hope Malleson tells us that "country people whose approval would carry weight in many circles" were invited, and *The Nursing Record* reported that the start of the meeting was delayed for half an hour by the late arrival of the guest of honour, Princess Mary, Duchess of Teck, who was one of Queen Victoria's favourite cousins and also the mother of Princess May of Teck (the future Queen Mary, consort of King George V). The Chair was taken by Sir Henry Longley KCB of the Charity Commission, and after Elizabeth had read a short account of how the movement had evolved, speeches were made by Mrs Ethel Bedford Fenwick, Lady Victoria Lambton and Miss Bertha Broadwood who had established a system of Cottage Nursing in Surrey. Mr G. Martin, who had replaced Mr Cox as Treasurer, summarised the proposed organisation of the scheme on a national level, and Dr Lowe, after describing the difficulties he experienced in attending widely-scattered cases in an agricultural district around Lincoln, formally proposed: "That this meeting is of the opinion that some definite organisation should be established for the purpose of bringing the benefits of good trained nursing at their homes within reach of the sick poor in rural districts." The resolution was carried unanimously, and on that day, Elizabeth Malleson's vision was finally embodied in a national charity, re-named the Rural Nursing Association (RNA). £800 was immediately raised and the list of Vice-Presidents, which heads the Constitution, included two Countesses, two Viscountesses and five Ladies.[37]

The Nursing Record expressed the opinion that the RNA "evidently requires a few Doctors and Nurses on its organising committee", but nursing historian Brian Abel-Smith points out that, once established at a national level, "the nursing reform movement ... was relatively swift because the pressure for it came from the top of the social hierarchy, ... the same social circle as the committees that ran [it]". Elizabeth Malleson had struggled for seven years to set up a successful charity; she had the ideas and the determination, but it required Lady Lucy's powerful links to turn her plans into reality. Elizabeth could not have called such an impressive meeting at the official residence of a member of the government, albeit a non-political gathering, and invite the Queen's cousin to attend, but Lady Lucy could.[38]

The combination of Elizabeth Malleson's tenacity and Lady Lucy's contacts and influence ensured that, as Hope Malleson tells us, "once started the Association grew apace", with existing rural schemes, "if in essentials conforming to the principles of the Association ... invited to join". Within a year, County Centres had been formed in Yorkshire, Hampshire, Pembrokeshire, Devon and Lincolnshire. Each county had a President and County Committee; the county was then divided into districts, each with its own Manager and Local Committee. This organisational structure reflected the importance of the social hierarchy as it then existed: at local level, the Manager of the District Nursing Association (DNA) was, more often than not, the local 'Lady Bountiful' and the Committee would consist of her daughters and worthy matrons such as the wives of the vicar, doctor and headmaster; at county level, representatives of the DNAs formed the County Committee, with the senior administrative posts filled by the ladies of the highest social rank and status, thus in Gloucestershire the County President was the Duchess of Beaufort and the Vice-President was Lucy, Countess St Aldwyn.[39]

Whereas Nurse Mary, the nurse employed by the Village Nursing Association, had lodged in the cottages of her patients at Gotherington, Elizabeth Malleson now "considered that there was not room enough in the average country cottage to accommodate a nurse, and that her maintenance was too great a tax at such a time". Each district nurse under the RNA was to be a visiting nurse only. She was to be provided with lodgings or a cottage of her own, and, under the terms of the Constitution, with the "means of her conveyance to distant parts of the district".[40]

Overall, the Association was controlled by the Central Committee, with Elizabeth Malleson as Secretary. This Committee, the Constitution states, "manages the business of the Association, receives Subscriptions, and decides upon the distribution of the General Fund, so as to encourage and assist local effort". The local committees were "to collect the local subscriptions, to receive the earnings of the nurse ... and to apply when necessary to the Central Committee for supplementary funds". The services of a trained nurse could "be obtained for from £50 to £60 a year. Part of this sum can be met by a graduated scale of fees charged for the midwife's services, the rest by local subscriptions, and in certain cases by a grant from the General Fund."[41]

In the Constitution, Elizabeth Malleson reiterated her original hope "that the General Fund of the Association will so increase as to enable its Central Committee to send suitable women from the country districts to be trained for the work". However, she also compromised on the alternate view by suggesting

> to ladies living in the country, who have taste and leisure to learn nursing, that such knowledge could be turned to excellent account in the houses of their poorer neighbours, (especially where sufficient

funds cannot be raised for the entire support of a nurse,) and would be an invaluable influence for promoting better modes of life among our rural population.[42]

The Association also encouraged "the giving of simple village lessons on the laws of health, and the economy of skilled nursing", and according to the Report of the Central Committee 1891, these had proved "efficient and satisfactory" where they had been tried "preparatory to the formation of districts, or as an introduction of the nurse". Between the autumn of 1890 and the summer of 1891, such lectures had been given in Gloucestershire, Wiltshire, Devon, Yorkshire and Wales.[43]

As well as producing the Constitution, Elizabeth Malleson also issued leaflets to arouse public interest and to guide local effort: *Hints for the Formation of County Centres*; *Hints for the Formation of Districts*; *Hints for Nurses*; and *Rules for Nurses*, the latter beginning with the directive that the nurse "must be an example of order, neatness, and helpfulness, must avoid gossip, and be careful never to interfere with the religious opinions of her patients".[44]

In addition to acting as Secretary to the Central Committee, Elizabeth Malleson also continued as Secretary and Manager of her own Gotherington District. In August 1889, Elizabeth and her Local Committee had engaged a new nurse, "Mrs Cotterill, trained as a Midwife at the British Hospital, London". The report for the year August 1889 to July 1890 records 984 visits by the nurse to "the villages of Gotherington, Cleeve, Alstone, Gretton with hamlets", including cases of bronchitis, pneumonia, jaundice, influenza, heart disease, burns and wounds. As well as nursing the medical cases, Mrs Cotterill had also "attended ten confinement cases in the year, which, as a beginning, is a fair number, considering that new plans and new people are met with some amount of prejudice, and that some little time is required for the women of the district to get accustomed to a stranger." For her services, the nurse was paid a salary of £1 a week and provided with a uniform costing £1.11s.9d. and instruments and dressings costing 15s.0d.[45]

Some residents "expressed surprise that the trained nurse does not undertake all the work of the house of her patients in addition to her own duties", as Nurse Mary had done, but Elizabeth now believed that "this cannot be reasonably expected from a woman skilled in her own business, nor from one who has other patients to visit". However, she expressed a hope that if "the Nursing Fund were to become rich enough to allow it, I, personally, should be glad to have a woman trained in sick and other cookery ... but I do not see my way to this fresh plan yet awhile".[46] No further reference is made to this additional helper in subsequent reports, so it must be assumed that this was one plan where lack of sufficient finances thwarted even Elizabeth Malleson.

The Report of 1890 stresses the need for further subscriptions, for "the nurse is maintained for the sake of every man, woman, and child in the villages ... for every one sooner or later must be ill, and those not sick can show compassion for those who are". Of the £59.14s.0d. listed as 'Subscriptions, Donations, and Thank-Offerings for Nurse's Services', £22.5s.0d. was contributed by Frank and Elizabeth Malleson, their daughters and members of the Whitehead family (relatives of Elizabeth).[47]

Despite its financial problems, the work of the Gotherington District was undoubtedly a success and it serves as an example of how, as Hope Malleson expresses it, "the Rural Nursing Association, brought to life with so much difficulty and opposition by one tenacious worker, grew in a few months into a big organisation with ramifications in many counties".[48]

Affiliation and Amalgamation

One of the first acts of the Central Committee of the Rural Nursing Association was to seek links with QVJI. Their first approach was made in June 1890, just a month after the inaugural meeting at 11 Downing Street, when, Hope Malleson tells us, "persons who knew the work of both Institute and Rural Association brought their various members together".[49] Miss Paget and Mrs Craven had both been amongst those who had given their names as approving the RNA; Lady Lucy Hicks-Beach worked closely with Elizabeth Malleson, whilst Sir Michael Hicks-Beach was a friend of Florence Nightingale; the Duke of Westminster worked tirelessly for QVJI, whilst the Duchess of Westminster joined the ever-growing and impressive list of Vice-Presidents of the RNA and served on its Central Committee. Furthermore, the two organisations shared the principles that the nurses must be trained, be supervised by ladies and should not interfere with the patients' religion. QVJI had always intended to extend into rural areas, but had concentrated on establishing itself in urban areas first. The leading figures of the RNA were able to present their charity as a ready-formed national rural scheme.

As an interim measure, the Institute awarded the RNA a provisional grant of £150, and a special sub-committee, consisting of the President, Vice-President and three trustees of QVJI, was set up to consider co-operation between the two schemes. There were fundamental differences which needed to be resolved before this could be achieved. In particular, whilst RNA nurses were allowed to supplement local funds by taking richer, fee-paying patients, the Conditions of Affiliation to QVJI stated that "the services of the nurses are to be strictly confined to the poor"; midwifery formed an important part of a RNA nurse's duties, but for QVJI nurses "in towns, attendance as a midwife upon women in childbed shall be excluded", although the nurse could attend a mother and infant after birth if a doctor "requires the services of a skilled nurse", i.e. if the mother and child needed medical attention as opposed to routine post-natal care.[50]

Fortunately, the sub-committee was sympathetic to the aims of the RNA and realistic in its understanding of the difficulties faced by a nurse working alone in an isolated rural area. The Conditions of Affiliation, which were published in March 1890, i.e. before the RNA meeting at 11 Downing Street, had already made provision for rural areas by stating that "nurses in country districts ... must have at least three months' approved training in midwifery", in addition to training in both general hospital nursing and district nursing. However, they stressed that "the duties of the midwife, as distinguished from a nurse, are not to be undertaken, except in cases of emergency, or by the express permission of the Local Committee". Queen's Nurses were, therefore, expected to be qualified for midwifery cases in rural areas as a precautionary measure, but midwifery was not acknowledged as a routine part of a district nurse's work.[51]

However, the sub-committee of QVJI had sufficient confidence in the principles of the RNA to designate it their Rural District Branch in 1891 and to embody in a Constitution, dated September 1892, its recognition of the need to compromise between what was desirable and what was practically possible in remote rural areas: "The support of a nurse, to a certain extent, may also be met by the fees, and by thank-offerings from patients, although the services of the midwives are intended for those who cannot afford doctors' fees."[52] As this applied to the majority of poor rural families, midwifery was clearly established as an integral part of a rural district nurse's duties.

Two clauses in Elizabeth Malleson's carefully drawn-up *Rules for Nurses* were duly amended. Under RNA rules, "The Nurse will be allowed to undertake cases of richer patients at ... 7s.6d. or 10s. a week, or more in exceptional cases"; as the Rural District Branch of QVJI, "The duties of the Nurse are to be confined to attending the poor of the district. But this is not intended to exclude cases of emergency, or of such patients as are in the opinion of the Committee able to make some contribution to the nursing fund". Most District Nursing Associations therefore adopted a sliding scale of annual subscriptions, dependent on income, with the poorest patients receiving free nursing care. Midwifery fees charged by the RNA were "5s. to those dependent on weekly wages, [but] in districts where the labourers' wages average less than 13s. or 14s. a week, the fees should be less in proportion". Under the auspices of QVJI, the fee of 5s. became standard and "as regards midwifery, all cases are excluded except those of the poor". In 1892-93, the weekly wage of agricultural labourers in the Midlands counties, including Gloucestershire, was 12s.6d., compared with the national average of 13s.4d. The introduction of a standard midwifery fee must, therefore, have placed a strain on family finances, at a time when Flora Thompson recalls that the 'old wife' of Lark Rise charged only half a crown (2s.6d.), for which "she officiated at the birth and came every morning for ten days to bath the baby and make the mother comfortable", but against this must be weighed the advantages of attendance by a trained midwife, compared with the conditions that Elizabeth Malleson had found when she moved to rural Gloucestershire. The Queen Victoria's Jubilee Institute for Nurses Rural District Branch *Rules for Maternity Nursing* state that the nurse "must go at once when summoned to a woman in labour. And she must not leave the case for at least an hour after delivery; and only then when she is assured of the patient's safety." Great emphasis was placed on the "conscientious practice [of] antiseptic midwifery", and there was to be no delay in sending for a doctor if complications arose. Post-natal care consisted of a visit "twice daily, Sundays not excepted", during which the baby would be washed and dressed, with special attention being paid to the cord, eyes and mouth, and the mother's "temperature and pulse are to be very carefully noted".[53]

The RNA application form for candidates was also amended to reflect the professional standards expected of QVJI nurses. Questions still included practicalities such as 'Are you strong and healthy?' and 'Are you a good walker, and accustomed to the country?', but the calibre of candidates was now further measured by the questions: 'What is or was the occupation of your father?' and 'Where were you educated?' Instead of merely enquiring about a nurse's training and experience to date, the form now began with a statement of the requisite qualifications:

(a) Training in some General Hospital, or Infirmary, for not less than one year.
(b) Three months approved training in Midwifery.
(c) Approved training in District Nursing.[54]

As a result of its affiliation with QVJI, Hope Malleson tells us, the Rural District Branch "received a yearly monetary grant, and its nurses benefitted by inspection in their work by one of the Institute's superintendents, but its chief gain was in being placed for all time upon a permanent footing, [whilst] the Branch continued its work as before, unhampered, with its own officers." It retained its own Central Committee and local structure, thus acknowledging QVJI's recognition of the importance and value of the social elite in rural areas. This was reflected in the list of RNA Central Committee members, Vice-Presidents and supporters which now included not only the Archbishops of Canterbury and York, and the Bishops of Salisbury and Peterborough, but also two Duchesses, nine Countesses, four Viscountesses and 17 Ladies. The meetings of the Central Committee were now held in London, where an office and secretary were installed at 12 Buckingham Street, and Hope Malleson herself moved to London "to take up the duties of Organizing Honorary Secretary, arranging and speaking at drawing-room meetings in various parts of the country".[55]

By September 1892, RNA nurses were working in 77 districts in 25 counties, including five in Gloucestershire in Gotherington, Kemerton, Quedgeley, Stanway and Westbury-on-Trym. This number may not seem impressive, as the result of two years work, particularly in view of the calibre of the RNA's patronage. However, in its Report of 1891, the Central Committee of the Branch explains that

> for the moment [it] is compelled to refrain from the active multiplication of districts and County Centres, because the demand for nurses, trained in midwifery, as well as in general sick nursing, has become so stimulated that a supply of suitable women is exceedingly difficult to obtain. They have now, therefore, to direct their especial attention to the training of nurses, a matter which takes many months to complete.

To Elizabeth Malleson and her fellow Committee members, quality was more important than quantity, if they were to help "individual districts to high class nurses, and ... to maintain that standard of thorough work to which the Association aspires".[56]

By 1896, a further 50 rural nurse/midwives had been trained and were working in 30 counties. The following year, the Council of QVJI approved the preliminary *Conditions of Affiliation for County Nursing Associations*, and in the interests of centralisation, complete amalgamation was recommended between the urban and rural branches under the one title of Queen Victoria's Jubilee Institute for Nurses. As Elizabeth Malleson tells us in her report of 1897,

> the rural districts of England and Wales, which had constituted a separate branch of the Queen Victoria's Jubilee Institute, were absorbed into the Institute; the Central Committee was dissolved, various members being placed on the Council of the Institute, and the Rural Branch became part of the magnificent nursing organization

originally planned by the Queen, alike for her poor subjects in rural districts as for those in towns.[57]

Thus, what began as a nine month experiment with one nurse in an isolated country village in Gloucestershire, became an integral and very important part of the national organisation from which today's system of district nursing has evolved. Elizabeth Malleson recognised the need for trained village nurse/midwives, and with resolute doggedness, she achieved her aim. In so doing, she not only overcame the disapproval of rural traditionalists, but she also created a new opportunity for the very social group that had initially opposed her. What motivated this change, and what both the Ladies Bountiful and the leading figures of QVJI aimed to achieve, will be considered in the next chapter.

THE QUEEN'S BAG.
Black or Brown COWHIDE, with extra outside pocket, removable washable lining. Very convenient for a cycle.

Notes

1. Hope Malleson, *Elizabeth Malleson: A Memoir* (Printed for Private Circulation, 1926), p.83.
   Lee Holcombe, *Victorian Ladies at Work* (Newton Abbot: David & Charles, 1973), p.5.
2. For a discussion of the Unitarian beliefs in which Elizabeth Malleson was raised, see:
   Kathryn Gleadle, *The Early Feminists: Radical Unitarians & the Emergence of the Women's Rights Movement, 1831- 51* (London: Macmillan, 1995).
   Barbara Leigh Smith, later Madame Bodichon, was the eldest of the five illegitimate children of Benjamin Leigh Smith, a wealthy merchant, and his mistress Anne Longden, a milliner's apprentice. One of Benjamin's nine siblings, Fanny, was the mother of Florence Nightingale, but the illegitimate branch was ostracised by the family and they did not mix socially. For full details of Barbara Leigh Smith's life, see:
   Sheila R. Herstein, *A Mid-Victorian Feminist: Barbara Leigh Smith Bodichon* (New Haven: Yale University Press, 1985), and
   Pam Hirsch, *Barbara Leigh Smith Bodichon 1827-1891: Feminist, Artist & Rebel* (London: Chatto & Windus, 1998).
3. Malleson, *Memoir*, pp. 124-5.
4. Ibid, p.115.
5. Jessica Gerard, 'Lady Bountiful: Women of the Landed Classes & Rural Philanthropy' in *Victorian Studies*, 30, Winter 1987, 183-210, (p. 192).
   Malleson, *Memoir*, p. 145.
6. Ibid, p.143-5.
7. David H. Aldred, ed., Gotherington Area Local History Society, *Gotherington: The History of a Village* (Stroud: Sutton, 1993), pp.90, 88, 89, 96 & 97.
8. Malleson, *Memoir*, p.146.
9. Aldred, *Gotherington*, p.100.
   Malleson, *Memoir*, pp.147-8.
10. Ibid, p.152.
    Lady Victoria Lambton & Mrs Elizabeth Malleson, 'Philanthropic Aspects of Nursing' in *Woman's Mission*, ed. by Baroness Angela Burdett-Coutts (London: Sampson Low, Marston, 1893), pp.206-215, (p.212).
11. Ibid, p.211-2.
12. GRO D4057/14 Gotherington album of documents re formation of Rural Nursing Association 1884-94.
13. British Library Add45808, F119-127 & F163-165v Letters from Elizabeth Malleson to Florence Nightingale 1888.

14. GRO D4057/14.
15. Ibid.
16. Zachary Cope, 'The Early History of District Nursing' in *Nursing Times*, 12 August 1955, 884-7.
17. Florence Nightingale, letter to *The Times*, 14 April 1876, p.6, c.4.
18. *The Lancet*, 22 April 1876, pp.610-611.
19. Rosalind Nash, ed., *Florence Nightingale to her Nurses: A Selection from Miss Nightingale's Addresses to Probationers and Nurses of the Nightingale School at St Thomas' Hospital, 1872-1888* (London: Macmillan, 1914), pp.45-7.
20. Cecil Woodham-Smith, *Florence Nightingale* (London: Book Club Associates, 1972 edition), pp.265 & 360.
21. Monica Baly, *A History of the Queen's Nursing Institute* (Beckenham: Croom Helm, 1987), pp.31-2.
22. *The Times*, 19 August 1887, p.7.
    F.K. Prochaska, *Women & Philanthropy in Nineteenth Century England* (Oxford University Press, 1980), p.17.
23. *The Times*, 3 September 1887, p.3, c.6.
    The Times, 25 August 1887, p.6, c.2.
24. *The Times*, 9 September 1887, p.3, c.3.
    The Times, 3 September 1887, p.3, c.6
25. Betty Cowell & David Wainwright, *Behind The Blue Door: The History of the Royal College of Midwives, 1881-1981* (London: Bailliere Tindall, 1981), p.22.
    Mary Stocks, *A Hundred Years of District Nursing* (London: Allen & Unwin, 1960), p.81.
    Baly, *Queen's Nursing Institute*, p.34.
    Gwen Hardy, *William Rathbone & the Early History of District Nursing* (Ormskirk: Hesketh, 1981), p.49.
26. GRO D2465 4/32 Cheltenham DNA Annual Reports 1880-1905.
    CRL 61G942CHA Mary Paget (ed.), Charlton Kings Local History Society, *A History of Charlton Kings*, (1988), pp.181-2.
    Malleson, *Memoir*, p.153.
27. Hardy, *William Rathbone*, p.6.
    Baly, *Queen's Nursing Institute*, flyleaf.
28. Malleson, *Memoir*, p.96.
    British Library, Add 45808.
29. Ibid.
    Woodham-Smith, *Florence Nightingale*, pp.3 & 449.
30. British Library, Add 45808.
31. Ibid.
32. Malleson, *Memoir*, pp.83, 91, 145, 153 & 207.
    British Library, Add 45808.

33. Malleson, *Memoir*, pp.145 & 153-4.
34. *The Times*, 26 September 1889, p.7, c.6.
35. *The Nursing Record*, 3 October 1889, pp.204-5.
    The Nursing Record, 17 October 1889, p.232.
36. Malleson, *Memoir*, pp.83-4.
37. Ibid, p.154.
    The Nursing Record, 22 May 1890, pp.246-7.
    GRO D4057/14.
38. *The Nursing Record*, 22 May 1890, pp.246-7.
    Brian Abel-Smith, *A History of the Nursing Profession* (London: Heinemann, 1960), p.36.
39. Malleson, *Memoir*, pp.154-6.
40. Ibid, p.155.
    GRO D4057/14.
41. Ibid.
42. Ibid.
43. Ibid.
44. Ibid.
45. GRO D4057/15 Gotherington Rural Nursing Association Annual Report 1890.
46. Ibid.
47. Ibid.
48. Malleson, *Memoir*, p.156.
49. Ibid, p.157.
50. Baly, *Queen's Nursing Institute*, pp.29-30 & 52.
51. Ibid, pp.29-30.
    Enid N. Fox, *District Nursing and the Work of District Nursing Associations in England and Wales, 1900-48* (PhD Thesis, London University, 1993), pp.41-2.
52. GRO D4057/14.
53. Ibid.
    Pamela Horn, *Labouring Life in the Victorian Countryside* (Dublin: Gill & Macmillan, 1976), p.259.
    Flora Thompson, *Lark Rise to Candleford* (Harmondsworth: Penguin, 1973 edition; first published 1939-43), p.135.
54. GRO D4057/14.
55. Malleson, *Memoir*, p.157.
    GRO D4057/14.
56. Fox, *District Nursing*, p.43.
    GRO D4057/14.
57. GRO D4057/15.

Elizabeth Malleson c1890
(Gloucestershire Archives D4057/25)

CHAPTER THREE
AIMS AND MOTIVATION

Lady Administrators

Historians generally agree on the reasons why middle and upper class ladies became involved in philanthropy. Stocks points out that many ladies became involved in rural district nursing "in the late 'eighties when the Jubilee Offering became 'news'". Gerard adds that "their patronage and presence on committees and boards were as much due to rank, wealth, and sense of duty, as to ability or interest", at a time when, Horn tells us, "titled ladies had a great deal of star appeal". Indeed, Fraser says that "in the 1870s and 1880s any charitable institution with a pretension to fashion is [sic] under the patronage of the royal Duchess of Teck, ebullient, extravagant mother of Queen Mary". The Duchess' presence as guest of honour at the inaugural meeting of the RNA in 1890 must have raised the profile of the organisation, but the long-term involvement of so many ladies with such philanthropic work cannot be explained merely in terms of royal sycophancy or publicity value. As Elizabeth Malleson stresses, in a paper which she wrote jointly with one of her co-workers, women who did become involved with nursing the poor "as a fashion ... [without] having any special aptitude or taste for the work ... must drop out of the ranks sooner or later, having no foundation for their brief enthusiasm".[1]

Elizabeth does not further define 'foundation', but Vicinus states that, within the cult of domesticity, the foundation of "all women's work was a sense of religious commitment". Prochaska agrees that "all Christian denominations stressed the importance of charitable conduct ... [as] synonymous with Christ-like conduct" and he adds that it "is a comment on the pervasive culture [that] ... there were women in nineteenth century England without religion, but ... they were few". Elizabeth Malleson was one of those few women. As an adult, she rejected her Unitarian upbringing and "ceased to consider herself a member of any religious body". Hope did not think that her mother "had any impulse towards corporate worship or felt the need of it ... [and] she could conceive of no personal communion by way of prayer". In religion,

> as in all else, she rated intellect very highly, and would have found it difficult to believe in the value of goodness not based on intelligence, or faith without reason behind it. ... She would have found it impossible to accept authority or the teaching of any sect in its entirety. ... Creeds, dogma, the attitude of the church-politic, meant nothing, or were felt to be antagonistic.

Instead, "her life was dominated by a high idealism, not a mere pious abstraction but a very real and practical sanction of daily and hourly conduct" and she brought up her own children to believe in "the *inevitableness* of duties and obedience ... of a high standard ... for its own sake". However, whilst Elizabeth was content to be inspired by a spirit of reforming endeavour and social responsibility, Hope tells us that this approach to life "did not prove sufficing to her children and they all took divergent paths." Hope herself became a Roman Catholic, which "was at first a grief and distress" to her mother, "but it left no lasting sadness."[2]

Nevertheless, Elizabeth's own lack of religious motives did not prevent her from working closely with Christian ladies. In view of her agnosticism, the closing appeal in a paper she co-authored with Lady Victoria Lambton, urging ladies to become involved in the administration of rural nursing associations, must be credited to Lady Victoria, who believed that they "may feel that they are obeying the injunction of our Lord, who said, 'The poor ye have always with you, and whenever ye will ye can do them good', and are following, in the way most suited to the present age and the present needs, His example, Who went about doing good, and healing the sick." The Hon Mrs John Dundas also referred to "the holy work of alleviating pain and suffering", whilst one of Elizabeth's most loyal local supporters was Anne Mercier, wife of the Rector of Kemerton, near Tewkesbury, who, Hope tells us, "backed her efforts through every vicissitude ... [with] so complete an understanding and sympathy and ... so large-hearted a tolerance that it overpassed the deepest divergence in religious opinions".[3]

Whilst women were expected to be religious, they were not expected to be political, beyond supporting the political aspirations and careers of male relatives. Elizabeth Malleson regretted that "in private talks" with county ladies, "political matters ... are taken with very aggravating passivity", whilst she felt them "as personal troubles". Nevertheless, she, a Liberal, worked in harmony with Lady Lucy Hicks-Beach, wife of a Tory minister, whom she described as "a splendid worker, with such knowledge of how success is to be won in the world, with entire freedom from worldliness or anything but large-heartedness".[4]

Unfortunately, not all ladies were so magnanimous and tolerant. At Stroud, two district nursing schemes were founded in 1894, the first by Florence Brynmor Jones, wife of the Liberal MP for Mid-Gloucestershire, the other by Mrs A.T. Playne, a Tory, working with the local clergy. When her husband lost his seat and the couple moved to London, Mrs Brynmor Jones was surprised to hear from committee member Mrs Winterbotham that the possible amalgamation of the two schemes was being discussed. In a series of letters, penned in bold, flowing handwriting, Mrs Brynmor

Jones' growing agitation is clearly conveyed by her liberal use of underlinings and double underlinings, which emphasise her disapproval whilst she purports to be unbiased. In November 1894, she wrote to Mrs Winterbotham:

> I hear a rumour that the opposition Scheme is in debt so if we amalgamate we must take care we do not become liable for their debts. I will leave it entirely with you and the Committee to decide about the joining of Schemes; whichever will be the best for the people of Stroud. I personally am not anxious to join as the other Scheme has been and is such a failure. Neither do I wish to resign my Presidentship at present or at all as if I did it would look as if mine Scheme were political (which you know it is not). ... I am very interested in my own Scheme and hope the Committee will see their way to do whichever is best for the prosperity of our own Scheme.

Although she insisted that Mrs Winterbotham and the Committee were free to vote as they wished, it is obvious that Mrs Brynmor Jones expected them to reject the amalgamation, whilst her reference to Mrs Playne and her supporters as 'the opposition' clearly negates her insistence that her aims were not political. Nevertheless, not only was the amalgamation approved, but a local clergyman, the Reverend Ormerod, was appointed President, with Mrs Playne as one of the two Vice-Presidents. In a clear fit of pique, Mrs Brynmor Jones wrote to Mrs Winterbotham in January 1895:

> I am glad you think the new Scheme is satisfactory on the whole and I hope it will work well. ... As my Scheme has been all altered ... I propose this year to send a subscription of 2 or 3 guineas. ... As now it is on such a much larger basis the funds I hope will be also on a larger scale as so many local Tories ought to give now Mrs Playne is a Vice President.

Mrs Winterbotham, herself elected as a member of the Executive Committee of the newly-named Stroud District Nursing Association, hastened to placate Mrs Brynmor Jones, pleading that the reduction of her subscription

> would place me and other friends of yours here in a very unpleasant position. On Nov 30th you wrote to me ... and said that though no longer a resident here, you did not wish at present or at all to withdraw from the scheme. ... On this insistence, at the Conference your name was linked with Mrs Playne's ... in [approving] the

> Amalgamation Scheme. ... We justified it in face of your having left the neighbourhood by a reference to your letter to me, to your own subscriptions and to your great and continued interest in the work. The new scheme is in all its essential features our scheme and ... you will see it will be a painful humiliation to me if your subscription is just now reduced. Subscriptions are now due and we need them; and if you will be so good as to continue your £10 sub ... I shall be encouraged and very much obliged.

However, her tactful, carefully chosen words elicited only a brief and peevish response:

> Although I approve of an amalgamation, still, of course, the Scheme now is quite different to what I originally started. ... I enclose a cheque of £5 and if at the end of 6 months the funds require more help, I will give another £5. I think as it is a local charity that really now it is on such a large scale the other side might help.[5]

Here, the correspondence ends and the name of Florence Brynmor Jones disappears from the records of the Stroud DNA. On the other hand, Mrs Playne, the object of her obvious contempt, remained its Vice-President, and also became President of the Nailsworth DNA when it was formed in 1899. In its report in 1920, it was recorded that of the twenty-one ladies who had been members of the Nailsworth DNA's first Committee, eight were still serving on the present Committee, "21 years of faithful service". In addition, Mrs Playne became a member of the General Committee of the Gloucestershire County Nursing Association when it was formed in 1905, a position she retained until her death in 1923. In their report of that year, the County Committee "deplore[d] the loss of an old friend". To such women, the welfare of the local community was more important than political affiliation.[6]

The formation of County Nursing Associations (CNAs), a progression of the RNA's County Centres, offered further scope for lady administrators as individuals whilst reinforcing the continued collective importance of the social elite in rural areas. As Stocks says, "in localities where the county aristocracy was still resident and locally active, ... district nursing provided an activity peculiarly suitable for local initiative. It was a new expression of the time-honoured concern of the great house for the cottage." Baly agrees that the "ethos of Victorian charitable visiting with its sturdy neighbourhood idiosyncracies and independence is the heritage of rural district nursing". With the formation of the RNA and its amalgamation with QVJI, the seal of royal approval and the financial security of royal patronage were added to rural district nursing, but the new system was grafted on to the old through the fusion of traditional benevolence with trained, professional efficiency. In this way, the prerogative and influence of the hierarchical society remained operational and the social fabric was not disturbed. At the same time, the quality of training, qualification, and subsequent day-to-day nursing was standardised on Nightingale lines by the requirement of annual reports from the DNAs and CNAs to the Council of QVJI and inspection of the nurses' work. The willingness of county ladies to accept this change in their role, from Ladies Bountiful personally administering to the sick poor, to lady administrators employing specially trained and professionally supervised nurses, reflects not only their recognition of the needs of the poor, but also illustrates their belief in their own ability to effect that change.[7]

Angela Burdett-Coutts, (1814-1906), herself a wealthy and generous subscriber to many charities, recognised the significance of this change in approach when she described women's philanthropic work in the 1890s as

> the continuation and development, under altered and more effective conditions, of a benevolence that deserves to be called historical. ... The same kindly feelings that work to such noble effect in the Englishwoman of to-day animated the Englishwoman of yesterday ... [who], moved by a conscious sense of responsibility, ... [dispensed] the kindnesses that are now recognised under the broad word Philanthropy.

Changes in society since the 1830s had, she continued, "enlarged the need of philanthropic activity", but at the same time, had "extended its means and multiplied its channels of operation. Especially have these changes worked in the direction of giving a collective form to efforts which were formerly left to individuals," who had worked "in the quiet, unimposing way which those times permitted, and which satisfied them". Baroness Burdett-Coutts was careful to include in her classification of philanthropic women not only the "immense middle class, vast in number and extremely well-to-do, [which] has arisen out of the ranks of the artisan and manufacturing class since Watt's tea-kettle filled his head with dreams", but also Queen Victoria who "stands foremost ... as representative philanthropist ... [and had] devoted the thousands which her countrywomen and subjects had offered ... on the completion of her Jubilee ... [to] the foundation of the Institute for Nurses". She concluded that all benevolent women shared a common philanthropic aim, which she describes in a phrase that pre-empts the National Health Service by fifty years: "the unity of feeling and of purpose ... directed to the amelioration, in the highest sense of the word, of the lives of our fellow-beings ... from the cradle to the grave".[8]

As philanthropy was a long-accepted part of Lady Bountiful's role, it was also an area in which neither the law nor social attitudes needed to be changed to permit women to work. In relation to their families, estates and local communities, the Ladies Bountiful were already engaged in supervisory and administrative tasks, but as Fraser points out, "it was rare, despite all the committees and societies and unions which ladies had joined so avidly, to find a woman presiding over the whole. The ancillary role of the Victorian lady, the convention of her dependence on her menfolk died hard." The Executive Committee of the MNA, chaired by the Duke of Westminster, was exclusively male. As previously noted, *The Times* automatically assumed that the advisory committee of QVJI would consist of gentlemen. Locally, throughout the period from 1880-1925, the Board of Governors of Cheltenham General Hospital was all male, as was the Committee of Tetbury Cottage Hospital, whilst the Committee of Fairford Cottage Hospital remained exclusively male until 1922, when three of its seventeen members were ladies. However, as Prochaska says, women came to challenge the view that "in the powerful world of organised charity ... their contribution might be superior in degree but it would be inferior in kind". Rural district nursing, as a new area of nationally organised philanthropy, offered county ladies a unique opportunity to establish themselves as administrators without being accused of challenging a recognised male preserve.[9]

When the Gloucestershire CNA was formed in 1905, only the Treasurer was male. The President, Vice-President, Hon Secretary and Assistant Hon Secretary were all female, as were all twelve members of the Executive Committee. Whilst the Duke of Beaufort was Patron of Tetbury Cottage Hospital, it was the Duchess of Beaufort who was President of the Gloucestershire CNA; Sir Michael Hicks-Beach, by then Earl St Aldwyn, was President of Fairford Cottage Hospital, but Lady Lucy, Countess St Aldwyn, was the CNA's Vice-President and Chairman of its Executive Committee.

It is interesting to note that, whilst the Gloucestershire CNA was being planned, the administrative arrangements at Fairford Cottage Hospital changed. Prior to that time, Lady Lucy had organised a rota of Lady Visitors, but in 1903, the visitors formed a separate Ladies Committee, headed by Lady Hicks-Beach. Their first act was a practical one: to order a new kitchen range to replace one that had been in use for more than twenty years and which, presumably, the all male committee had deemed still adequate. In the Annual Report of 1904, it was noted that

> the Ladies Committee have met regularly every week to go over the housekeeping books and superintend domestic affairs generally. This has permanently lightened the labours of the General Committee, who highly appreciate the interest which the Ladies take in the Institution, and the work which they have done and are doing to increase its efficiency and usefulness.

It is surely more than a coincidence that Lady Lucy's increased responsibility at Fairford Cottage Hospital and the formation of the CNA should happen simultaneously. Sir Michael Hicks-Beach and the Duke of Beaufort both made generous donations to the County Fund, but it was their wives who ran the CNA. Lady Lucy eventually resigned as Chairman of the Executive Committee in December 1920, explaining that she was "no longer young and was becoming somewhat deaf and rather blind". Of the twelve ladies who had formed the first Executive Committee fifteen years earlier, seven were still serving members and five were present at the last meeting that Lady Lucy chaired, when the Duchess of Beaufort recalled that, "though she herself was always deeply interested in district nursing, the CNA had been very specially the child of Lady St Aldwyn, for which she had worked with her whole heart, and that to a very great extent it was due to her that the work had prospered and increased". Although she retired from the Executive Committee, Lady Lucy continued to serve as the CNA's Vice-President, with the Duchess as President, and both were still in office in 1925. In addition, Lady Lucy served as President of her local Coln St Aldwyn, Eastleach, Hatherop, Quenington & Southrop DNA from its formation in 1910 and chaired its regular Committee Meetings until the 1930s. Nationally, she was also a member of the Council of QVJI and served on one of its Working Committees.[10]

It could, of course, be said that such privileged ladies, each with a houseful of servants and an assured income, had ample leisure hours to devote to charities, but philanthropic work was not a trivial pursuit. It represented a means of satisfying the basic human urge to be needed and useful, and it was undertaken as a deliberate alternative to leisure activities such as playing the piano, arranging flowers or reading frivolous novels. Most nineteenth century philanthropic women retained a hierarchical view of society, with its accompanying overtones of *noblesse oblige*, but if a positive sense of duty had been their only motivation, they could have continued in their traditional role of Ladies Bountiful. In running DNAs and CNAs, women of intelligence, energy and initiative saw the possibility and seized the opportunity to provide the sick poor with modern nursing care whilst, at the same time, as Gerard says, "expand[ing] their [own] lives beyond the limited domestic role prescribed for them, gaining opportunities not only for altruism, but for leadership, authority and power. This was real, valued work, requiring time, effort, and skills; it was both demanding and fulfilling."[11]

It may seem surprising that Gloucestershire, where the RNA began, did not have a CNA until 1905, but at "a Meeting of ladies interested in District Nursing" held in Gloucester in 1904 to discuss the formation of a County Association, the Duchess of Beaufort, in the Chair, explained that "the idea of such an Association for Gloucestershire was one which she and Lady Lucy Hicks-Beach had long had in their minds, but had refrained from starting till the calls connected with the South African War and the Queen's Memorial Fund were at an end". Considering the tenacious determination with which Elizabeth Malleson established the rural district nursing scheme, the fact that she was not more closely involved at county level may also seem surprising. However, her daughter Hope tells us that she was not influenced "by personal ambition, and it may be said without exaggeration that she never made a decision from a worldly motive". She was "singularly modest about her own achievements" and was satisfied that "her enthusiasm, her dominating personality, her confidence inspired others to embrace her schemes, working with her or following where she led".[12]

When the RNA had affiliated with QVJI as its Rural District Branch, "it became apparent to E.M. that the work was hampered by having the honorary secretary in the country and its superintendents and secretary in London". In 1893, "as the future of trained nursing in the country was now happily assured, she decided to retire from the post of honorary secretary". However, Hope continues,

> the announcement was received almost with consternation. 'The Rural District Branch is your own child,' members of the committee wrote to her. 'It owes its existence to you, and its growth is entirely due to the great time and thought you have devoted to its affairs. ... The actual daily working must be to you such a source of interest and satisfaction.'

She was begged to continue, to give the work the "benefit of her counsel, and this she did, remaining an active member of the Central Committee", until the amalgamation in 1897, when, as previously noted, the Committee was dissolved. By this time, Elizabeth Malleson was sixty-nine years old. For health reasons, she and her husband Frank had spent the winter months of 1894/5 and 1896/7 in South Africa, staying with their son Rodbard, who had emigrated there in 1893 to join one of his maternal uncles, Percy Whitehead. In 1899, Elizabeth suffered "a dangerous illness which left such a prostrating weakness that for some time the struggle back to her usual occupations seemed an unbearable effort"; then in 1903, Frank died of influenza and "with her husband's death the light went out of E.M.'s life. There remained a resolute courage and that constraining sense of her obligations to others which imposed upon her an outward serenity ... [but] her life was maimed beyond remedy."[13]

With her advancing years, Elizabeth relied increasingly on her daughters. Rachel, the second daughter, had married in 1881 and lived at Oxford, but Mabel and Hope remained single and worked closely with their mother. From their early teens, they had all been expected to share in their parents' strenuous life at Wimbledon. "To teach self-reliance and independence was part of our parents' scheme of education," Hope recalls, and Elizabeth "never considered youth and inexperience in themselves a bar to the assumption of responsibility". The sisters were expected to represent their mother at various committee meetings, taking and reading the Minutes, and though "our way often took us through 'slummy' parts of London, ... neither parent would hear of timidity or hesitation". Although Hope rarely criticises her mother in the biography, she does admit that the children did, on occasion, encounter the "prejudice [which] would sometimes arise to mar E.M.'s openness of mind and her sympathy, often only for a time", and she suggests that "it is perhaps a legitimate criticism of this system" of education for life, with its emphasis on personal responsibility, both for actions and consequences, "that it may weigh too heavily upon a child's conscience, its emotion and susceptibilities, and bring in its train a habit of introspection". It would appear that the independence which Elizabeth encouraged in her daughters was still confined within the boundaries imposed by her own sense of duty and altruistic motives.[14]

Hope's involvement in the district nursing scheme has already been noted in Chapter Two, but Mabel Malleson also played an active part. Although Elizabeth had made the opening speech at the inaugural meeting of the RNA in 1890, it was Mabel who spoke on her behalf at a meeting in Gloucester in February 1893 when the formation of a County Centre was first discussed. "Mabel said a few words for me," Elizabeth recorded. "It was impossible for me without pressure, which would have made me ill, to write anything as asked." When the Gloucestershire CNA was formed in 1905, Elizabeth sat on the General Committee as the representative of Gotherington DNA, but Mabel sat on the Executive Committee and was still a member in 1925.[15]

Elizabeth remained Manager of the Gotherington DNA, where "the burden of managing the affairs of the district, receiving the nurse's reports and inspecting her books, raising the money and replacing the nurse when a change was necessary, issuing the yearly report and balance-sheet, fell almost entirely upon E.M.'s shoulders - no light task for one of her age!" To ease her burden, in 1905, an Advisory Committee of ladies, including her daughter Mabel, was formed to assist her, though she continued to write the Annual Report. Their aim, Elizabeth explains, was "not to disturb the present organization of the work, but to give it increased support in advice and practical help". The following year, she

> rejoice[d] with some wonder at the enormous progress made ... in late years. When the first Report of this district was issued in 1890, the matter was regarded here, as a rule, with distrust, if not with hostility. At the present time, we live under a whole-linked system, recognising and supporting the efficiency of nursing. ... The Gloucestershire County Nursing Association ... is working steadily month by month with admirable ability and devotion under the guidance of the Duchess of Beaufort and Lady St Aldwyn and a capable, strenuous Executive.

Elizabeth retained her interest and influence in rural nursing until she died in 1916, at the age of eighty-eight. On her death, "far and near the loss was felt as a personal grief and calamity, and it was realised that ... [her] place could never be filled".[16]

Stocks concludes that "for close on thirty years" Elizabeth Malleson "had played a lady's part in the history of district nursing and justified the social and economic privilege that enabled her to play it". However, Elizabeth was also very aware of the injustices of social privilege. As her daughter Hope expresses it: her "natural aristocratic instincts ... had always oddly antagonized with her belief in democracy". She believed, with Lady Victoria Lambton, that each rural district nursing scheme "must be a charity ... [because] the poor are utterly unable to pay for skilled attention in serious illness", yet she disapproved of social moves towards rectifying such poverty, particularly where militant methods or government intervention were involved. Hence, she condemned Trade Unions as an "unpatriotic and ignoble force", believed that "Lloyd George seems to have found fresh means of making daily life more anxious and difficult - in his insurance of every possible human creature!" and regarded "with some apprehension" the introduction of the first maternity benefit, writing in her Report of 1913:

> Hitherto the months of expectant motherhood have afforded a time for thrift and management, costing happy care and thought, as good for the mother as for the expected child, and the tax paid to her by the rest

of the population, appears a slur on parental care and foresight, which we trust will not have the bad effect that might be feared upon this and the coming generation.

As early as 1889, Elizabeth had predicted that the "many ladies who bury themselves in out-of-the-world villages by choice, or who find themselves naturally so buried ... would find a hitherto unknown happiness" in administering rural district nursing schemes, and Gerard believes that "they found this work personally fulfilling and rewarding ... [because] they felt they were effective not only in ... ameliorating the lives of the poor ... [but also in] preserving the traditional social relationships of authority and deference". Speaking in 1905, the Dean of Gloucester described the Duchess of Beaufort and Lady Lucy Hicks-Beach as "altruists ... [who] were trying to help their poorer brothers and sisters", and it was their social position that gave such ladies the power, resources and influence to ameliorate the problems caused by that very class gulf.[17]

The titled ladies who became the Vice-Presidents of the RNA and the Rural District Branch of QVJI were not mere figureheads. Hope Malleson tells us that they "helped to further the objects of the Branch" by writing letters and articles in the press, publishing pamphlets and speaking at meetings and conferences throughout the country. Gerard adds that this "competence in counselling, teaching, planning, organizing, and public speaking gave them greater self-confidence and self-esteem, enabling them to seek wider public roles in organized philanthropy". In the words of the Dean of Gloucester, "they were all - Roman Catholic and Protestant, Whig and Tory - they were all agreed that the poor had been helped and would be helped in the most efficient manner by District Nursing Associations". To the lady administrators of DNAs and CNAs, philanthropy represented a personal choice of positive action, a collective aim which overcame both doctrinal differences and political affiliations, allowing them to practice their compassion for the poor whilst, as Stocks says, enabling them "to share the satisfaction enjoyed by their brothers, husbands, and fathers, of expressing their personalities in constructive organization". The national system of district nursing could not have been so successfully established in rural areas without them.[18]

The Nurses

Social historian Ross McKibbin suggests, somewhat cynically, that "the function of the first generation of district nurses ... was never really to bring the wonders of modern medicine into the slums of Britain but to stop people behaving (as they believed) stupidly". In her letter to *The Times* in 1876, Florence Nightingale expressed it rather differently:

> Now, what is a district nurse to do? A nurse is, first, to nurse. Secondly, to nurse the room as well as the patient - to put the room into nursing order; that is, to make the room such as a patient can recover in; to bring care and cleanliness into it, and to teach the inmates to keep up that care and cleanliness. Thirdly, to bring such sanitary defects as produce sickness and death ... to the notice of the public officer whom it concerns.

To achieve these dual aims of curative care and preventative education, the district nurse must look for the means of mitigating suffering, even in incurable cases, and teach by example,

> to sweep and dust away, to empty and wash out all the appalling dirt and foulness; to air and disinfect; rub the windows, sweep the fireplace, carry out and shake the bits of old sacking and carpet, and lay them down again; fetch fresh water and fill the kettle; wash the patient and the children, and make the bed. ... And it requires a far higher stamp of woman ... thus to combine the servant with the teacher, and with the gentlewoman, ... [and] command the patient's confidence ... than almost any other work.[19]

This belief in the seemingly innate ability of educated ladies to influence the behaviour of the lower classes through the power of social example was further expounded by Elizabeth Malleson in relation to district nursing. Even when she initially preferred the idea of training a local woman as a district nurse, Elizabeth believed that, "in the fulfilment of her ordinary duties, [the nurse] must tend to humanize and improve the home life of the cottagers". In the Preliminary Prospectus of the VNA (1884), the patronising term 'humanize' has been omitted and it is suggested that "a kindly Nurse living amongst cottagers would also become a valuable influence in the spread and observance of sanitary knowledge". The Constitution of QVJI's Rural District Branch (1892) adds that "ladies living in the country ... would be an invaluable influence for promoting better modes of life among our rural population". By the following year, 1893, Elizabeth Malleson believed that "if by our philanthropy we wish to raise and improve the condition of the poor, to teach them by example to live healthy and more refined and orderly lives ... no nurse is too good, too refined, and too high-minded for the work".[20]

From its instigation, the Committee of QVJI recommended that its nurses "should all be duly approved women of excellent personal character, and of good education". In its comment on this announcement, *The Times* assumed that "bearing in mind what are the highest attributes of feminine character," QVJI would "provide a congenial vocation for numbers of refined and good women, and enable them to indulge their tenderest instincts unclogged by pecuniary considerations. ... And some of the atmosphere of refinement which may be expected to surround a Queen's nurse will stay in the house when the nurse's mission is ended and she is gone." In a letter to the newspaper, an unidentified doctor stressed that it was "manifestly essential" that such representatives of "Her Majesty's benevolent desires" should be "in all respects worthy, ... in good health, of good character, of assured sobriety", whilst the Treasurer of the North London Nursing Association added that "this class of superior nurses" should be so "worthy and self-sacrificing" that the idea of "making broad her phylactery" would be "generally distasteful" to them.[21]

From these comments it can be seen that, despite the general agreement that the aim of district nurses should be to improve the lives of the poor as well as caring for them, there was a clear difference of opinion concerning motivation. On the one hand, the media and public were calling for a pseudo-religious order which reflected the belief that philanthropy was the highest expression of women's 'natural' virtuous traits. On the other hand, Florence Nightingale envisaged paid professionals who were, nevertheless, inspired by a sense of calling. She believed that as "man cannot live by bread alone ... [so] woman does not live by wages alone". She recognised the danger that district nursing could be seen by young women as the means "to have a life of freedom, with an interesting employment, for a few years - to do as little as you can and amuse yourself as much as you can". Echoing Elizabeth Malleson's views of lady administrators who became involved in rural work as a fashion, Nightingale warned of the danger of district nurses responding to "fashion ... [with] its consequent want of earnestness ... [and] the enthusiasm which every one ... must have in order to follow her calling properly". She reiterated her definition of the purpose of district nursing by differentiating between nursing the sick ("to help the patient suffering from disease to live") and what she called 'health-nursing' ("to keep or put the constitution of the healthy child or human being in such a state as to have no disease"). By that time, Nightingale was also advocating the employment of health-missioners. These were to be educated ladies who were not nurses but who would be trained to give lectures and instruction to the poor on sanitation and hygiene. She acknowledged that such women might prove difficult to find in sparsely populated areas, and she stressed that, in isolated rural communities, the district nurse "also should be a health missioner as well as sick-nurse". By acting as "missioners of health-at-home", district nurses had the opportunity to address at first hand the social evils of "dirt, drink, diet, damp, draughts, [and] drains", and to achieve this

> the nurse must have method, self-sacrifice, watchful activity, love of the work, devotion to duty, ... courage, ... the tenderness of the mother, the absence of the prig ... and never, never let the nurse forget that she must look for the fault of the nursing, as much as for the fault of the disease, in the symptoms of the patient.[22]

Florence Nightingale's views were formally embodied in *A Guide to District Nurses and Home Nursing*, a manual which Mrs Craven was asked to write for the use of QVJI nurses in 1889, and which Nightingale proof-read. Nightingale's influence is clear, particularly where Craven stresses that a district nurse must be motivated by

> a real love for the poor, and a real desire to lessen the misery she may see among them. ... Her aim must be not only to aid in curing disease and alleviating pain, but also through the illness of one member of a family to gain an influence for good so as to raise the whole family. ... Wherever a district nurse enters, order and cleanliness should enter with her ... [and] every poor person should be as well and as tenderly nursed as if he were the highest in the land.[23]

Both Stocks and Baly praise Craven as a paragon of district nursing, the former describing how, "when she entered a sickroom kindness and competence shone in it like a burst of sunlight through mist ... [and] her nurse trainees felt at once the guidance and encouragement of a master hand". However, her approach appears to have been of the brisk and efficient, 'Nanny knows best' variety; for example, she suggests that if a patient insists that he has already washed that day, "the nurse should say pleasantly, 'Well, we needn't do your face again, then; but we mustn't let you get bed-sores, you know, so I will just ... put you in nursing order.'" She believed that

> the very essence of district nursing is, that a nurse should have such tact as well as skill that she will *do what is best for the patients*, even against their will, knowing how to manage the weakest and most irritable, and doing all that is necessary for them ... as she often has to teach her patients and their friends the simplest sanitary rules.

Her definition of 'tact' was questionable: whilst working as Superintendent General of the MNA, Craven (at that time Miss Lees) did not always work in harmony with its all male Executive Committee. She had a strong personality and could be blunt, and Nightingale often had to mediate. When Craven became Hon Inspector of Nursing for the MNA in 1880, as Stocks expresses it, "those who fell below her standards or pursued a course other than as directed, emerged from the experience as crushed worms". Nevertheless, Craven's manual reveals her to have been a highly skilled nurse in practical terms, conscious of nursing ethics and adept at improvising equipment. Although her approach could hardly be described as subtle, she was clearly motivated by genuine, noble intentions. She saw district nursing as "too high and holy" a calling to warrant any aim other than the highest possible standards and she expected the nurses to share her views. All QVJI trainees were requested to read Craven's manual and her influence on the earliest Queen's Nurses is without doubt.[24]

In contrast with Craven's patronising, nannying methods, a manual written by Margaret Loane in 1905 urges a more realistic approach:

> The practical nurse will, of course, understand that there are few cottages in which it will be possible for her to carry out every detail of nursing with the perfection to which she has been trained. ... The most successful district nurse is the woman ... who knows what *ought* to be done, but can cheerfully reconcile herself to what is practicable in any given case.[25]

McKibbin describes Miss Loane (18??-1922) as one of "the most accomplished Edwardian practitioners of a cultural sociology", whose observations were "neither sentimental nor condescending". The date of Loane's birth is unknown, but her father was a captain in the Royal Navy and she spent her early life in Portsmouth. She trained as a nurse at the Charing Cross Hospital and worked as a Sister both there and at the Salop Infirmary before training as a district nurse. She then worked both in rural and urban areas before returning to Portsmouth as Superintendent of District Nurses. Loane recognised that "even the most skilled hospital nurse is likely to feel herself at a loss when beginning to work in a district" and the aim of her book was "to aid the nurse in adapting herself to these altered conditions, to teach her to utilise such things as may be found in almost every house, and to do it without loss of time or sacrifice of efficiency".[26]

On her first visit to a new case, the district nurse should impress herself upon the patient, family and friends "as a kindly and capable woman, trustworthy, anxious to help, ready to acknowledge the value of all that has already been done, not likely to 'make more work 'n she saves', and neither gullible nor unreasonably suspicious". Loane stresses the importance of showing respect for the patient and her home, for it was possible for the nurses "to be both well-bred and tender-hearted and yet not be acquainted with the precise forms that will be most acceptable to a poor person when they visit her house ... in their professional capacity". On arrival, the nurse should tap politely on the door, remembering that "in knockerless, bell-less regions ... a never-to-be-departed from etiquette demands that only the hand should be used". She must take care to use the patient's name, for "among the poorer classes it is clung to with extraordinary persistency. To call a person 'out of her name' is unpardonable, not to call her by it early and often is scarcely less wounding to her feelings." The nurse's voice should be "carefully lowered" for "not only an authoritative loudness is disliked" by the poor in their social superiors, "but that particular shade of tone and manner which ... is 'kindly condescension'. The manner to be cultivated is simple and unaffected, but qualified by extreme gentleness."[27]

Treatment and care should be "gentle, skilful, and carried out in a calmly assured manner". Loane emphasises the importance of a fixed routine and uniformity of method, but warns that

> many district nurses offend their patients and strew their own path with thorns by a too rigid insistence on matters desirable but not of the first importance. In things essential the nurse should strive her utmost to keep up to the best hospital standard, but there are many comparative trifles ... [where] constant concessions may be made.

For example, on a hospital ward all beds would be made uniformly, "but that is not the smallest reason why Mrs Jenks of 4 Picks Court, enthroned in her own bedroom in her own house, should have the counterpane an inch straighter than she wishes, nor why, as she graphically expresses it, she should be 'laid out afore she's dead'".[28]

In conclusion, Loane reminds the district nurse that she

> is merely an advisor and cannot immediately expect to be a trusted one. ... Confidence grows slowly and can never be forced. Perhaps it may be the fifth, perhaps the tenth visit, and the nurse is not yet permitted to do all that instinct, training and experience tell her to be desirable; but surely slow and real progress is preferable to forcing her will upon the friends at the first visit, being plainly shown at the second that she is unwelcome, and at the third being plainly told so? The poor will always be grateful for a courtesy that constantly keeps in remembrance the facts that they are in their own house, [and] that they have a 'right' to do almost exactly as they choose.

The nurse must, therefore, approach each case "with cheerful and indomitable patience", always remembering that "she works by influence, not authority, and that real and lasting influence can only be in proportion to the respect and liking that her patients have for her".[29]

By 1924, the aims of the district nurse were still seen as "not only the treatment of disease, but the education of her patient and his friends in the essentials of hygiene so as not only to prevent all avoidable infection but to raise the standard of health in each household she visits". In a handbook compiled by 'Some Queen's Superintendents', the ideal district nurse is described as possessing

> the qualities of tact, patience, discretion, adaptability, and common sense, with sound health and a real love of humanity. ... She must bring keenness and enthusiasm to her duties and must be equal to speaking, as occasion arises, with clearness and wisdom on the principles of right living and a better standard of life. Her manner should be gracious and her judgment sound; she must be tactful in dealing with all those with whom she comes in contact, and be very discreet both in speech and behaviour.[30]

When visiting a new case, the district nurse "should make friends with the patient and find out how much it is necessary and wise to do at a first visit". Her foremost thought

> must be for her patient ... and should he not see the need of all she knows to be necessary for his comfort and recovery, she must go to work very tactfully, carrying out her duties with kindness and common sense. She should give every consideration to his wishes, yet so manage that nothing essential or helpful to him is left undone: indeed the patient's approval of her procedure should be won.[31]

For the first time, the handbook emphasises that "the mental attitude of the patient must always be taken into consideration", particularly chronic patients, many of whom "improve very much when their minds are occupied in some way, so she can suggest and often teach some occupation, such as knitting or crochet." In conclusion and above all, the nurse must remember that

> she has to rely on her powers of persuasion to win the confidence of her patient. By her way of living, her personal neatness, her friendly and discreet conversation, her courtesy and consideration, she will be judged, and on these qualities will depend the influence she is able to exercise in a community.[32]

Where the second official aim, of 'health nursing' was concerned, Craven emphasised that

> a very necessary part of the duty of a district nurse is to make herself acquainted with the sanitary, as well as charitable, agencies of the district or districts where her work lies. Wherever she finds the water supply defective, drains untrapped or badly trapped, cesspools and dustbins unemptied, etc., she should write to the medical officer of health, and if the defects complained of are not remedied she should then write to the sanitary committee of the district (if there is one), who will take legal steps, if necessary, to compel the landlord to put the premises into a proper sanitary condition.

Loane's only references to other agencies involve informing the Medical Officer of Health of infectious cases such as smallpox or typhus, and following the death of a patient from typhoid, scarlet fever or phthisis, "the nurse should persuade the friends to apply to the sanitary authorities to have the room disinfected. In country districts the nurse can disinfect a room herself." With regard to seeking charitable support, "let her always think of the aged first, and remember that the one comfort they yearn for is a fire". The Superintendents advise that the nurse "should be conversant with the work of the statutory Authorities dealing with the health of the nation ... and the many Voluntary Societies in existence ... and she should co-operate in a friendly way with their officials".[33]

Thus, the aims of the ideal district nurse remained unchanged, but in the thirty-five years from 1889, when Craven's manual was published, to 1924, when the Superintendents compiled their handbook, the approved method of achieving those aims progressed from telling the sick poor what to do and complaining to the authorities, via offering professional advice and employing persuasive communication, to friendly co-operation with all concerned.

However, whether the majority of district nurses achieved the official aims and maintained such high standards is debatable. Baly believes that "for all their educational aims it appears that theory and practice were often divorced". Craven recalled

> with some dismay the look of satisfaction on a nurse's face as she took me to a new case of chronic bronchitis, where she had arranged the room by herself. Every bit of carpet, all bed-hangings, curtains, and what the nurse termed unnecessary furniture, had been removed into the family sitting-room, which resembled chaos, and where the father and children had hardly room to move. The bedroom had been wiped over with a very damp cloth, and still looked damp.

The nurse was most surprised when the patient announced that she preferred her young daughter to look after her and no longer required the nurse's services.[34]

Loane had "a smarting recollection" of a first visit paid by one district nurse who "knocked loudly and peremptorily on the door with the handle of her umbrella. It was immediately opened by a tidy but worn looking woman of about forty. Without a word of courtesy, of explanation, of preface of any kind, the nurse said in abrupt, impatient tones, 'Nurse wanted here?'" Having gained entry, the nurse proceeded to treat both the woman and the patient, her bed-ridden mother, with "profound disparagement" and would have refused to accept the case had not Loane personally intervened. On another occasion, she supervised "a visit paid by a nurse who had had seven years' experience in one of our largest London hospitals", yet showed total disregard for even the most basic rules of hygiene, tossing towards the fire both dirty dressings and cotton wool used to clean the wound, "some reaching it, some not".[35]

Writing in the first issue of the *Queen's Nurses' Magazine* in 1904, Amy Hughes, General Superintendent of QVJI from 1905 to 1917, felt the need to remind district nurses that "by joining the Queen's Institute, ... each nurse becomes a steward to faithfully carry out a trust", passed down to them in Florence Nightingale's vision of health missioners. Hughes asks:

> Has each of us realised her personal responsibility in these matters? Does every one of us feel conscious that the technical nursing and practical care of patients are not the end of our work, but only an introduction to a wider field of duty in every home we enter? Unless every Queen's Nurse does grasp this fact she has missed the reason of her special training.[36]

Loane warned that "an ignoble jealousy and a desire to magnify our own importance sometimes stand in our way as teachers", and that sense of elitism was further threatened by the introduction of a second grade of district nurse in rural areas. The anomaly of rural district nursing lay in the fact that, in the areas where the nurses were most needed, the poor patients could least afford to subscribe to local funds, and many DNAs found themselves unable to pay the wage for a Queen's Nurse (QN). In addition, many of the nurses were reluctant to work in isolated rural areas and found the responsibility of midwifery daunting. In an attempt to solve these problems, under the Conditions of Affiliation for County Nursing Associations, first issued in 1897 and revised in 1901, the Council of QVJI sanctioned

> the employment of Village Nurses in rural districts where it is impossible to support a Queen's Nurse and the population of the district does not as a rule exceed 3,000 ... or in a rural district in which a Queen's Nurse is already employed and where there is a demand for the services of a Village Nurse to work under her directions.

These Village Nurse-Midwives (VNMs), as they soon became known, were not hospital-trained nurses. They were local working class women who were to have no less than six months' and preferably nine months' training in district nursing, and in addition hold the Certificate of the London Obstetrical Society or other approved midwives' certificate. The VNMs were to work under the supervision of the County Superintendent, who was herself under the supervision of the QVJI Inspectors. The County Superintendent was to be a Queen's Nurse with the midwifery training required for a rural post, and her appointment by the CNA required the approval of the Council of QVJI.[37]

Loane stressed the importance of such teamwork:

> Egoism forbids co-operation, and without co-operation no great achievement is possible. The doctor cannot do everything, neither can the nurse nor the relatives, there is even something left for the patients themselves to do; but if every one will accept their due share of work and responsibility, then, and only then, will the invalids be thoroughly well cared for.

However, there was clearly a widespread feeling of resentment amongst the QNs, who regarded the VNMs as professionally inferior due to their lack of hospital experience. These feelings were made clear in an unattributed article in the *Queen's Nurses' Magazine* of 1910:

> The work of County Nursing Associations is not very cordially accepted by many Queen's Nurses. There is a prevalent uneasy idea that the Queen's Institute in recognising these Associations and their 'Village Nurses' has departed from its original standard, and approves that much-scorned individual, the 'half-trained nurse'.

The article reminds its readers that the supervision of VNMs by the County Superintendent "has helped in a marked degree to raise the general standard of work", and reassures them that, in rural areas "where it is not possible to provide work and funds to justify the employment of a Queen's Nurse, the village nurse is a valuable factor, filling a real need, and under wise supervision taking her share in building up the health of the community."[38]

Despite the official support for VNMs, professional jealousy persisted amongst the district nurses. When Queen's Nurse Margaret Powell became an Assistant Superintendent to the Gloucestershire CNA, it was noted that she was "not always tactful in dealing with Village Nurses". At a Conference of Queen's Superintendents in 1913, "a lack of sisterly kindness on the part of some Queen's Nurses to their less trained sisters" was noted, and amongst the questions discussed was: "Can we remove the spirit of opposition that exists in our midst against the employment of inferior trained nurses by County Associations?" Unfortunately, neither the points raised in the discussion nor the conclusion reached are recorded, but the fact that the matter was discussed at "one of the largest gatherings in the history of the association", attended by Rosalind Paget and Amy Hughes, illustrates both the extent of the problem and the seriousness with which it was regarded by the most senior members of QVJI.[39]

A further cause of resentment was the introduction of Public Health Work after 1908. Concern over the poor physical condition of army recruits during the Boer War (1899-1902) generated a comprehensive national programme to improve the health and welfare of the young. This involved health visiting, maternity and infant welfare clinics, school nursing and tuberculosis care. It represented an extension of Florence Nightingale's vision of district nurses as 'health-missioners', but the work was regarded by many of the nurses as less interesting and less important than nursing care. One Queen's Nurse noted that "each development on the social side has met with a certain amount of opposition at its first introduction, but each succeeding year has shown how indispensable the new departure has proved to the health of the community". She acknowledged that a district nurse "will not get the same kudos" for preventative work as she would "for one patient snatched from the Gates of Death", but she urged:

> Let her realise that it is in the power of the district nurse to prevent suffering to a degree that is hardly to be estimated, and surely she will feel that the 'health' work she may be called upon to do as school nurse, as midwife, as tuberculosis nurse, as health visitor or inspector under recent legislation, is to the full as important as that which is generally regarded as 'more interesting'.[40]

One Inspector attempted to quell ill-feeling and motivate the nurses by appealing to them in verse, albeit very bad poetry:

> We are the Nation's Missioners,
> So it behoves that we
> Should always try and do our best
> And bright examples be.

Don't let us grumble if we're asked
Some other work to add,
Tuberculosis and the schools,
It really makes us sad

To think that legislators
Were compelled to make new laws
To keep our people clean and well,
It shows there were some flaws.

I think you will agree with me
If we all pull together,
The sooner we shall reach the shore,
In spite of stormy weather.[41]

In their handbook, the Superintendents reminded district nurses of the importance Florence Nightingale had attached to preventative work and they suggested that "in rural districts ... the combination of duties gives variety and interest to a post". The *Queen's Nurses' Magazine* also reminded its readers of Nightingale's original dual aims for district nursing, of curative care and preventative education. In 1923, the magazine reprinted extracts from Nightingale's letter to *The Times* of April 1876, and stressed that, after nearly fifty years, the ideals she expressed should still be the motivating force behind the Institute's work, for "conditions change with the times, but it is in details and not essentials that the work has developed".[42]

One Queen's Nurse who did approach her work with the loyalty and fortitude that Florence Nightingale envisaged was Agnes Hunt. She was born in 1867, one of eleven children, ten of whom survived childhood. Her parents owned estates in Shropshire, Leicestershire and Northamptonshire, and the family lived at Boreatton Park, Baschurch, Shropshire, which Agnes described as "one of England's stately mansions, surrounded by broad fertile acres of land, the home of our race for many generations. We had indoor and outdoor servants to minister to our needs, hunters, carriage horses and ponies for our use." She reminds her readers that, at that time, "daughters of the upper middle class were not supposed to go out into the world to earn their own living". However, her mother, a stern, formidable, sixteen-stone martinet, "was a law unto herself, and I well remember the stinging lecture ... [which] ended with these words ... 'I refuse to have any daughter of mine sitting round with her mouth open, waiting to be married.'"[43]

Agnes completed her training as a Lady Pupil at the Salop Infirmary in 1891, and after working as a Staff Nurse there for eight months, she trained as a Queen's Nurse at Hammersmith, then obtained the midwifery certificate of the London Obstetrical Society. At Hammersmith, she met Emily 'Goody' Goodford, daughter of the Provost of Eton. They became close friends and worked together as Queen's Nurses in both rural and urban areas until 1900. Of their work as district nurses, Agnes wrote: "The work was hard but intensely interesting. Here I realised for the first time the tremendous scope and power of a nurse's life. One went into those homes, not as 'my lady bountiful', but as a fellow human being, a friend to give personal help, to teach and to serve." Agnes recalls that "my work on the district had made me realise the bitter difference between the life of a crippled child brought up in a slum, and my own sheltered girlhood". She increasingly felt a "call to help" disabled people which "rang clear and strong, until it became a positive obsession". In 1900, she opened the Baschurch Home, with the encouragement and support of eminent surgeon Sir Robert Jones and with Goody as her key-worker. Over the next twenty years, this developed into the renowned Robert Jones & Agnes Hunt Orthopaedic Hospital at Oswestry, to which both women devoted the rest of their lives.[44]

The few district nurses who have left a record of their thoughts and experiences tend to be either those who rose to high office within QVJI, such as Florence Craven and Margaret Loane, or who enjoyed distinguished careers, such as Agnes Hunt, who was made a Dame of the British Empire for her work with disabled people. As such, they could be said to be as unrepresentative and atypical a minority as were the negative examples. The silent majority of district nurses were, no doubt, unassuming and industrious, like Queen's Nurse Ann Newdick who took up her post in Charlton Kings, Gloucestershire, in September 1909 and remained until she retired twenty-four years later in August 1933.

Ann was born in 1868, the daughter of a farmer and corn merchant. After being educated at Shrubland House, Soham, Cambridgeshire, Ann worked as a Children's Nurse until the age of thirty-six. From 1904-7, she trained as a general nurse at Mill Road Infirmary, Liverpool, then in 1908 she trained as a district nurse and midwife with the MNA in London. During her district training, Ann was noted to be "a quiet, steady worker, capable and conscientious nurse, liked by her patients". In September 1908, Queen's Nurse Newdick took up a post in Cheltenham, where her work was "thoroughly and well done", though it was noted that she was "very slow", then in September 1909, she transferred to Charlton Kings DNA. Her inspection report for 1910 reads, "Much improved in every way. Working up the district well," and subsequent reports describe her as "kindly and attentive", "a good, steady and capable nurse, with a pleasant, sympathetic manner". However, whilst she was recognised as being "most conscientious" and having "a high standard", Nurse Newdick was also regularly criticised for being "slow" and, after almost twenty years in her post, she was regarded by the Inspectors as "old-fashioned" and reluctant to "grasp new ideas". Nevertheless, she was "very popular", "well appreciated" and "much respected" by her patients, amongst whom she exercised a "good influence".[45]

This view of her is confirmed by Mary Paget, who was delivered by Nurse Newdick on a Sunday morning in 1912:

> I remember Nurse Newdick very clearly. She was heavily built and gave the impression of being slow, but she was absolutely wonderful and much respected in the village. She never forgot any of the numerous babies she had helped into the world. She thought of us as 'her' babies, and if ever my mother and I saw her in the street, she always stopped and talked to us.[46]

After Nurse Newdick retired in 1933, at the age of sixty-five, she continued to live in the village and died there in 1955, at the age of eighty-seven, having devoted almost her entire career as a district nurse to the people of Charlton Kings. It was of such nurses Sydney Holland said, at a presentation of badges and certificates by Princess Louise at Kensington Palace in 1899, that they "were not angels, and that they resented very much the sort of exaggerated language often used about them and their profession. They were loyal, noble, and devoted women, working ... to lessen misery and suffering."[47]

The translation of theory into practice was affected by the realities and practicalities of working with the poor in their own homes, but the majority of district nurses did their utmost to fulfil their duties to the best of their abilities.

Notes

1. Mary Stocks, *A Hundred Years of District Nursing* (London: Allen & Unwin, 1960), p.92.
   Jessica Gerard, 'Lady Bountiful: Women of the Landed Classes & Rural Philanthropy' in *Victorian Studies*, 30 (Winter 1987), 183-210 (p.184).
   Pamela Horn, *Ladies of the Manor: Wives & Daughters in Country-house Society 1830-1918* (Stroud: Sutton, 1991), p.112.
   Flora Fraser, *The English Gentlewoman* (London: Guild Publishing, 1987), p.12.
   Lady Victoria Lambton & Mrs Elizabeth Malleson, 'Philanthropic Aspects of Nursing' in *Woman's Mission*, ed. by Baroness Angela Burdett-Coutts (London: Sampson Low, Marston, 1893), pp.206-215, (pp.209-10).
2. Martha Vicinus, *Independent Women: Work & Community for Single Women 1850-1920* (London: Virago, 1985), p.37.
   F.K. Prochaska, *Women & Philanthropy in Nineteenth Century England* (Oxford University Press, 1980), pp.8, 11 & 13.
   Hope Malleson, *Elizabeth Malleson: A Memoir* (Printed for Private Circulation, 1926), pp.76-7 & 216-7.
3. Lambton & Malleson in *Woman's Mission*, p.215.
   The Times, 26 September 1889, p.7, c.6.
   Malleson, *Memoir*, p.154.
4. Ibid, pp.160, 224-5 & 227.
5. GRO D2774 6/1 Papers concerning Stroud DNA 1893-5.
6. GRO D3548 3/1 Nailsworth DNA Annual Reports 1900-48.
   GRO D4057/1 Gloucestershire CNA Annual Reports 1905-31.
7. Stocks, *District Nursing*, p.92.
   Monica Baly, *A History of the Queen's Nursing Institute* (Beckenham: Croom Helm, 1987), p.49.
8. Burdett-Coutts (ed.), *Woman's Mission*, pp. ix-xxi.
9. Fraser, *English Gentlewoman*, p.167.
   Prochaska, *Women & Philanthropy*, p.17.
10. GRO D1070/VII/91 Fairford Cottage Hospital Annual Reports 1870-1923.
    GRO D2410 Minutes of Gloucestershire CNA 1904-28.
11. Anne Summers, 'A Home from Home: Women's Philanthropic Work in the Nineteenth Century' in *Fit Work for Women*, ed. by Sandra Burman (London: Croom Helm, 1979), pp.33-63, (p.38).
    Prochaska, *Women & Philanthropy*, p.125.
    Robert Dingwall, Anne Marie Rafferty & Charles Webster, *An Introduction to the Social History of Nursing* (London: Routledge, 1988), p.28.
    Gerard, 'Lady Bountiful', p.209.

12. Reprinted from *Gloucestershire Chronicle*, 24 September 1904, Hicks-Beach private family papers.
    Malleson, *Memoir*, pp.96 & 83-4.
13. Ibid, pp.158-9 & 213-5.
14. Ibid, p.77, 92-3 & 140.
15. Ibid, p.158.
16. Ibid, pp.161 & 163.
    GRO D4057/15 Gotherington DNA Annual Reports 1890-1916.
17. Stocks, *District Nursing*, p.104.
    Malleson, *Memoir*, pp.204 & 226.
    Lambton & Malleson in *Woman's Mission*, p.214.
    GRO D4057/15.
    Letter from Elizabeth Malleson to *The Nursing Record*, 17 October 1889, p.232.
    Gerard, 'Lady Bountiful', p.207.
    Report of the First Meeting of the Gloucestershire County Nursing Association, 1 February 1905, Hicks-Beach private family papers.
18. Malleson, *Memoir*, p.157.
    Gerard, 'Lady Bountiful', p.206.
    Report of the First Meeting of the Glos CNA.
    Stocks, *District Nursing*, p.17.
19. Ross McKibbin, *The Ideologies of Class* (Oxford University Press, 1991), p.177.
    Florence Nightingale, letter to *The Times*, 14 April 1876, p.6, c.3 & 4.
20. Elizabeth Malleson, letter to *The Cheltenham Examiner*, 28 November 1883, p.8, c.5 & 6.
    GRO D4057/14 Gotherington album of documents re formation of the Rural Nursing Association 1884-94.
    Lambton & Malleson in *Woman's Mission*, p.214.
21. Letter to *The Times*, 7 January 1888, p.8, c.1.
    The Times, 7 January 1888, p.9, c.1 & 2.
    Letter to *The Times*, 18 January 1888, p.9, c.6.
    Letter to *The Times*, 21 January 1888, p.4, c.6.
22. Florence Nightingale, 'Sick-Nursing & Health-Nursing' in *Woman's Mission*, pp.184-205.
23. Mrs Dacre Craven, *A Guide to District Nurses & Home Nursing* (London: Macmillan, 1894 edition), pp.1-6.
24. Stocks, *District Nursing*, p.42.
    Craven, *A Guide*, pp.5-12.
    Baly, *Queen's Nursing Institute*, pp.14 & 15.
25. Margaret Loane, *Outlines of Routine in District Nursing* (London: Scientific Press, 1905), p.vii.

26. McKibbin, *Ideologies*, pp.169 & 189.
    Loane, *Outlines of Routine*, pp.vi-vii.
27. Ibid, pp.139-143.
28. Ibid, pp.6 & 158.
29. Ibid, pp.145-50.
30. Some Queen's Superintendents, *Handbook for Queen's Nurses* (London: Scientific Press, 1924), pp.45-6 & 29-30.
31. Ibid, pp.37 & 44-5.
32. Ibid, pp.37, 45 & 56.
33. Craven, *A Guide*, pp.10-11.
    Loane, *Outlines of Routine*, pp.50 & 135.
    Superintendents, *Handbook*, p.39.
34. Baly, *Queen's Nursing Institute*, p.37.
    Craven, *A Guide*, p.38.
35. Loane, *Outlines of Routine*, pp.139-140 & 160-1.
36. Amy Hughes, 'Some Responsibilities of Queen's Nurses' in *Queen's Nurses' Magazine*, Vol 1 Part 1, (May 1904), 11-13.
37. Loane, *Outlines of Routine*, p.153.
    GRO D4057/14.
38. Loane, *Outlines of Routine*, p.152.
    Unattributed, 'County Nursing Associations & Their Work' in *Queen's Nurses' Magazine*, Vol VII Part 1, (April 1910), 9-11.
39. Contemporary Medical Archives Centre Records of Queen's Nurses (hereafter CMAC) SA/QNI/J.3/13.
    Unattributed, 'The Conference of Queen's Superintendents' in *Queen's Nurses' Magazine*, Vol X Part 2, (April 1913), 35-37.
40. Q.N., 'Some Reminiscences - And a Moral' in *Queen's Nurses' Magazine*, Vol X Part 4 (October 1913), 97-98.
41. An Inspector, 'Queen's Nurses' in *Queen's Nurses' Magazine*, Vol X Part 1, (January 1913), 23.
42. Superintendents, *Handbook*, p.71.
    Unattributed, 'Trained Nursing for the Sick Poor' in *Queen's Nurses' Magazine*, Vol XX Part 4 (November 1923), 165-166.
43. Agnes Hunt, *Reminiscences* (Shrewsbury: Wilding, 1935), pp.41 & 70.
44. Ibid, pp.77 & 119.
45. CMAC SA/QNI/J.3/15.
46. Interview 17 Jan 2003.
47. *The Times*, 6 July 1899, p.8, c.2.

CHAPTER FOUR

THE NURSES: PROFESSIONAL AND SOCIAL STATUS

Relationships with Doctors and Committees

As early as 1879, *The Lancet* predicted that the belief "that a governess should be looked down upon, while a lady-nurse is regarded as a heroine, is an anomaly due to a fashion which, like other fashions, will have its day". The clear assumption in that statement is that a governess and a nurse were *both* decidedly inferior as they contravened the fundamental doctrine of domesticity, that a lady should not work. A post as a governess, a ladies maid or a private nurse had long been accepted as a suitable occupation for an educated lady in financial need because, although it was paid employment, she remained within her 'proper' sphere, the home. However, a governess' position within her employer's family was one of incongruity, as defined by one contemporary social observer: "She is not a relation, not a guest, not a mistress, not a servant - but something made up of all. No one knows exactly how to treat her." 'Lady helps' and ladies' maids also found themselves in an ill-defined position where any attempt to preserve an air of gentility appropriate to their station could be interpreted as arrogance by the other servants. One titled lady said of the governess, "the servants invariably detest her, for she is a dependent like themselves, and yet, for all that, as much their superior in other respects as the family they both serve", but a gardener from Winchcombe recalls that "the most hated servant of all was the lady's maid. This was so in most big houses. *Nothing* escaped her eyes and her tongue wagged unceasingly." Private nurses, whilst they could boast of professional training and status, were also in an incongruous position between mistress and servants. A private nurse was not a devoted spinster relation, but she was expected to display ladylike manners; she was not a domestic servant, but was expected to manage a working class workload. In such a hostile atmosphere, with fewer places available as they grew older, and the prospect of old age without a pension or a home, the situation of such ladies was notoriously bleak.[1]

By comparison, the district nurse did not live with her employers or patients. Her sphere of work was still within the home, but she was a visitor, practising the sympathies and skills supposedly inherent in women's nature. However, she was not Lady Bountiful; she was a specially trained nurse and her introduction into a district was often met with hostility by local doctors, who felt threatened by these new professionals. In the late nineteenth century, most medical practitioners came from the professional classes; they were the sons of tradesmen or of intelligent artisans. Many of the nurses, trained and educated under the Nightingale system, were from at least an equivalent if not a higher social background than doctors, at a time and in a society where men still expected to dominate. Furthermore, doctors had only been recognised as members of a registered profession since the passing of the 1858 Medical Act which established a General Register for practitioners holding qualifications from degree and diploma granting bodies recognised by the newly-formed regulatory body, the General Medical Council (GMC). The subsequent increase of 53% in the number of doctors in the thirty years after 1861, from 17,300 to 26,500, may have raised their social prestige and sense of self-importance, but it also created competition for patients and fees.[2]

In addition, many doctors believed that the limits of medical and surgical advances were about to be reached. As one surgeon wrote in 1873, "That there must be a final limit to development ... of our profession there can be no doubt. ... That we have nearly, if not quite, reached these final limits, there can be little question."[3] This, of course, was at a time when the uterus was regarded as the cause of all female illnesses, though the functions of the ovaries and fallopian tubes were not even vaguely known and there was incomplete understanding of the menstrual cycle, with the middle of the month believed to be a woman's 'safe period' when, in fact, it was her most fertile time.

Nevertheless, doctors felt defensive, both of their knowledge and professional position. The improvements in the training and status of hospital nurses had already roused medical opposition; the district nurses posed a new threat. In 1896, one doctor wrote to *The British Medical Journal* condemning "that craze which is at present affecting a certain section of fashionable society for putting women in positions of authority ... which practically place them on a level with, or superior to, the medical staff". He scathingly describes "the modern nurse, with her grand get-up, her waistbelt with a surgical instrument maker's shop dangling to it, and her array of temperature charts and thermometers", and concludes that "the whole nursing sisterhood is being far too much pampered and petted. ... It is a most unfortunate movement ... [and] it is our duty to make a distinct stand against this sort of thing." In its early stages, the progress of nursing as a profession had possessed a negative advantage: nursing had always been considered 'women's work' and was not, therefore, considered a threat to male employment, but with the introduction of district nurses, particularly in rural districts where GPs did not enjoy the same status and incomes as their urban counterparts, doctors feared that the nurses might become serious rivals and undercut their fees. One doctor complained that, since the introduction of a district nurse in his parish, "my midwifery practice is virtually nil". He dismissively referred to "the Jubilee midwifery nurses (I am not sure of the name they bear)" and condemned their work: "The professional nurse with her thermometer and her tongue is bad enough, but the certificated midwife is an outrage on the medical practitioner." Another GP, Dr Robert Rentoul, contemptuously declared that he was "sick of all this cant about poverty; if the working-class smoked and drank less, they could easily pay the doctor".[4]

It was Dr Rentoul who also led a petty campaign by a faction of the GMC to have the diploma of the London Obstetrical Society (LOS) outlawed in 1894, on the grounds that it was a 'colourable imitation' of a medical diploma. He succeeded in having the wording of the award amended and the diploma printed in a smaller format, but the examinations continued, and the diplomas were still awarded. However, those holding this midwifery qualification

> were warned not to use the letters 'L.O.S.' after their names since some innocents - or less innocent and more determined doctors - were claiming that these letters represented not the 'London Obstetrical Society' but 'Licentiate of the Obstetrical Society', and that this must imply that the midwives were claiming to have a 'licence to practice' in rivalry to the medical profession.[5]

Lady Victoria Lambton of Pembrokeshire, speaking at a conference in Liverpool in 1891, expressed her unpleasant surprise and regret that doctors opposed the appointment of district nurses, instead of recognising their value and appreciating their help. She acknowledged that, "the midwives do take some of the doctor's fees, and as a country doctor's practice is not always very renumerative, they have perhaps a little reason to complain; but on the other hand the nurse saves the doctor many a long drive or ride to attend patients who would probably never pay him." However, some doctors did recognise the benefits of trained district nurses and welcomed their help, for the very reasons that Lady Victoria suggested. In the Gotherington district, Hope Malleson tells us, the "medical practitioners [were] often poorly qualified and always overworked, their time taken up by driving long distances to their patients at all hours of the day and night through dark and steep lanes", and in 1891 Elizabeth Malleson "gratefully acknowledge[d] the increased support of the trained nursing given by the medical men attending patients in the District".[6]

In its first report of 1905, the Gloucestershire CNA emphasised that, when starting a DNA, the Committee should "hold one or more small meetings to discuss the matter with those interested, especially the medical men of the district" and that a VNM, with her shorter training, should only be employed "with the sanction of the medical men of their district". The CNA's Constitution included a clause stating that "certain medical men of the County to whom appeal may be made on technical matters when necessary" should be invited to become members of its General Committee, and regular reference is made in the Annual Reports to the Committee's "appreciation of the never-failing courtesy and most valuable advice and interest in every detail of the work given by the County Medical Officer of Health - Dr Middleton Martin". Furthermore, the rules for DNA's affiliated to QVJI stated that "application for the services of the nurse may be made direct to her or otherwise. The nurse may attend a patient on application or in emergency, but must not continue to visit without informing a medical man and receiving his instructions, if any." The officially recommended working relationship was, therefore, clearly one of co-operation and communication between the doctors and nurses.[7]

In reality, however, clashes occurred: at Painswick, in 1900, it was recorded that "some difficulty having arisen owing to the Nurse having been kept waiting at the Doctors Surgery for orders, the Committee agreed it would be better that the Doctor should in future leave written orders for the Nurse with the patients". Unfortunately, Dr Ferguson refused to agree, "owing to the greater trouble it would entail on him". Unperturbed, "the Committee informed him that ... if he would not give Nurse orders she must work under orders from the Committee". Faced with such an unequivocal ultimatum, the doctor appears to have acquiesced, as it was then agreed "to provide slates to be left at the house of each patient upon which the doctor could leave his instructions and on which Nurse could make notes of temperature, etc".[8]

In midwifery cases, QVJI rules stated that the district nurse "shall not accept an engagement without first asking the patient to state and herself registering the name of the doctor to be called in should any emergency arise". When the Committee of Upton St Leonards DNA wrote to four local doctors in 1904, requesting their co-operation in this scheme, all agreed "to attend in maternity cases at a fee of £2.2s.0d. to include attendance for 10 days", but one, Dr J.R. Bibby, insisted that "of course, the message would be sent during the day" and only Dr W. Jones displayed compassion for the poor by adding that "I shall be only too pleased to attend a really deserving case at any time at a reduced fee".[9]

Despite such outward co-operation, professional rivalry and jealousy continued to simmer throughout the county until, in 1910, Dr Douglas E.

Finlay, Hon Secretary of the Gloucestershire Branch of the British Medical Association (BMA), wrote to the Gloucestershire CNA:

> Re rule that Nurse may not attend a patient more than once without the sanction of a Doctor: I am asked to inform the County Association that three cases have come under my notice quite recently, and in one, the Nurse wrote to the Doctor asking him to give a prescription for a patient, who had been ill for more than a week, diagnosing the case for the Doctor.

Dr Middleton Martin, the County MOH, attempted to act as a diplomatic, supportive intermediary, writing to Amy Hughes, Superintendent General of QVJI, in March 1910:

> I am not quite certain in my own mind that the British Medical Association are well advised in the attitude that they have taken in this matter, for there are probably many cases in the practice of a District Nurse in which she can be of considerable service to her patients and in which the attendance of a doctor is quite unnecessary and attendance on which the Local Practitioner would in many cases consider it not his duty.

The Gloucestershire CNA attempted to compromise by adding a rider to the rule, stating that "this rule is not intended to preclude the nurse from giving friendly help in cases of trifling ailments and accidents, such as would be attended to by a good children's nurse in any large household". However, in December 1910, Dr Middleton Martin wrote to inform the Committee that

> I am sorry to tell you that the Gloucestershire Branch of the BMA declined to accept the rider of the County Nursing Association to the Rules of the QVJI by 18 votes to 2. If all the statements made last night are strictly correct, I am afraid the nurses in the county have many sins of commission and omission to their account: I am, however, inclined to consider there is another side to the story which was not brought out.

When the opinion of Miss Hughes was again sought, she wrote to Mrs McCormack, the County Superintendent, in January 1911:

> I have not heard any expressions of opinion from the County Superintendents about the nurses attending small dressings for minor

> cases without a doctor. I do not see that there will be the difficulty you anticipate: the rule of the institute has always been that nurses must work under the medical practitioners. Unfortunately, in some cases this has not been observed, and there has been a decided increase in the number of supposed minor cases in which the nurses - village more than Queen's - have prescribed when really it was the beginning of a serious case. ... There is practically no difficulty in a nurse having attended a cut or broken chilblain and telling the mother what to do, mentioning the fact to the doctor when she next sees him or, if writing to him about anything else, telling him what she has done. There was an instance not long ago of a bad scratch causing tetanus: this may be an extreme case, but one never knows what poison may be contracted by a simple wound. ... There is really no reason to be alarmed, only to be specially careful to impress upon the nurses they must not undertake cases and prescribe and treat for patients without the knowledge of the doctor.

Clearly satisfied with the legality of their stance, a resolution was passed at a Committee Meeting of the Gloucestershire CNA on 15th February 1911: "In view of the refusal of the BMA to agree to the suggested liberal interpretation of Rule V this meeting of representatives of local nursing associations recommends the County Association to inform the BMA that they cannot conform to this Rule in its present form." Although the Secretary of the Gloucestershire BMA acknowledged receipt of the CNA's letter, by April 1911 no formal, detailed reply had been received. An unnamed doctor (though, in view of his sympathetic opinions, it was most likely the MOH) unofficially informed the CNA that the BMA had "decided to do nothing about it but to wait for 'any case' of a nurse attending a patient without a doctor being notified, to arise, and then a fuss would be made. The sense of those present was that the 'case' should be other than something trivial." The CNA responded to this warning by sending a circular letter to all local DNAs, urging them "to take every care that your nurse gives the doctors no cause for dissatisfaction, but carries out the spirit of the rule and the rider which was proposed by our Committee".[10] It would appear that the nurses complied, as no further correspondence on this matter survives, and at Painswick in December 1911, the Chairwoman "reported that there had been no complaints from the doctors of Nurse attending cases for which they should have been called in".[11]

By 1918, Rosalind Paget felt able to write in the *Queen's Nurses' Magazine* that initially

> the medical profession looked askance at the question [of nurse/midwives] because ... they were dreadfully afraid of giving any status to [them] ... for fear that the latter should enter into competition with them. All this is now changed. ... The importance to the community of the self-respecting, competent and intelligent nurse/midwife is self-evident.

Baly believes that this "progress was made ... thanks to ... the squirearchy and the nobility who ran the local associations and the tact of the inspectors". At both Winchcombe and Painswick, the inclusion of the local doctor's wife on the DNA Committee was doubtless of value in encouraging co-operation, but negative pressure could also be brought to bear. One doctor described how, when asked if he was willing to be called to births in cases of emergency, he "declined emphatically to the secretary, who is a lady of good social position and the wife of a retired Q.C. ... and since then I have been boycotted both socially and professionally".[12]

Such intervention by the Committee could also be a mixed blessing for the nurse, particularly if, as was more often than not the case, the Manager of the DNA was also the local Lady Bountiful who expected to be privy to every aspect of the villagers' lives. The Gloucestershire CNA's Rules for Local Associations include the directive that "the Nurse ... shall consider as strictly confidential all matters which shall come to her knowledge concerning her patients", whilst the Superintendents pointed out that

> the Committee are working with the same object in view as the nurse ... and the one could not exist without the other. Their relations should be frank and cordial, and while the Committee assist the nurse, as far as a lay Committee may, she on her part should endeavour to see the work from their point of view and to co-operate in a loyal way.

The district nurse could easily find her loyalty to her patients compromised by having to report confidential matters to the DNA Committee which, as well as Lady Bountiful and her daughters, often included the local vicar's wife and doctor's wife.[13]

Individual clashes of personality, regional traits and a lack of knowledge of local customs could also affect a nurse's relationship with a Committee. Nurse Mildred Griffiths (Gotherington 1911-14) was noted to be "inexperienced in country work", with a "somewhat irritating and self-opinionated manner". Jessie Douglas was also "inexperienced in dealing with country people" when she took up her first post as a QN in 1911, and whilst working at Gotherington from 1914 to '15, her reports read "manner brusque, temperament lethargic" and "not very enthusiastic or sympathetic". However, when she returned to her native Scotland, she was reported to be "careful, interested and much-liked". During twenty years as a QN in urban posts in the north of England, Catherine Phillips was regarded as "a clever, capable nurse", "a very careful maternity nurse and a pleasant woman", "kind, willing to please". Yet, when she briefly worked for Nailsworth DNA in 1923, she was described by the Hon Secretary as "untidy and unprincipled" and by the County Superintendent as "unreliable and of a difficult temperament". Nurse Helen Moore (Upton St Leonards 1903-07) was "inclined to gossip", Rose Paling (Lydney 1921-37) was "inclined to talk too much" and "resenting authority", whilst Beatrice Price (Stone 1920-38) was "somewhat secretive in manner".[14]

A district nurse's professional position was both delicate and unenviable. She was expected to co-operate with the local doctors, whilst employed by the DNA Committee, and working under the supervision of the County Superintendent. At all times, she was also expected to maintain her professional integrity, and respect the confidentiality of her patients. Furthermore, the nurse's difficult professional position could also be complicated by her social status.

Social Background and Training of Queen's Nurses

Depending on the attitude of the DNA Committee members, a district nurse could also find herself in the incongruous social position experienced by other working ladies. 'Lady helps' and ladies maids often chose to eat their meals away from the other domestics, in an attempt to preserve their status and self-respect. Similarly, in 1896, Lady Priestley complained that a private nurse she had employed "was too educated and high-class to fit into the household and that she would not eat with the servants". The fact that Lady Priestley clearly *expected* the nurse to eat with the servants is as significant as the nurse's refusal. Her ladyship's attitude was certainly not unique, as Stroud DNA considered it necessary to include in their *Terms and Rules* the directive that, if a district nurse attended a paying patient, she "should take her meals out of the Patient's room, and apart from the Servants". Agnes Hunt describes herself as upper middle-class, but when she arrived for an interview at Rushden in Northamptonshire in 1892, wearing her Queen's Nurse's uniform, the supercilious butler at the Treasurer's imposing mansion ordered a liveried footman to escort her to the servants' hall, where she was kept waiting for an hour. When finally she was taken, not to the drawing-room, but to the dining-room, "the door was flung open and the Hon Treasurer swept into the room". At the end of the interview she "gave me a solemn warning not to become too friendly with Mrs and Miss Sartoris, who, as she told me, were the big landowners of the district, and naturally much above the position of a district nurse".[15]

In Gloucestershire, attempts were clearly made to accommodate the nurses socially after the *Queen's Nurses' Magazine* had highlighted the problem that, in rural districts, "there is often but little opportunity of any social intercourse with congenial spirits. This is a real deprivation to many nurses who have been accustomed to some such relaxation in their leisure time." From 1911, a Garden Party was held each summer, to which all the district nurses in the county were invited, though in 1913 it was noted that "all were most enthusiastic in their appreciation of this enjoyable gathering, the only regret being that more nurses were not able to be present owing to the demands of their work and the difficulty of railway communications in the country districts". In that year, Mrs Cadogan of Hatherop loaned her motor car to enable the two nurses of the Coln St Aldwyn, Eastleach, Hatherop, Quenington & Southrop (CEHQS) DNA to attend. This annual event was cancelled in 1915, owing to the war, and appears not to have been revived after 1918, though individual ladies continued to invite the nurses in their district to tea, including Lady Lucy Hicks-Beach, the Countess St Aldwyn, and Mrs Dent-Brocklehurst of Sudeley Castle in Winchcombe. However, whilst such entertainment was clearly provided with the best possible intentions, it was, nevertheless, a separate social provision, not inclusion. Similarly, Flora Thompson recalls the day of the annual Manor House treat in Lark Rise, when the schoolchildren were feasted in the servants' hall whilst other guests were served tea in the drawing-room. When the new schoolmistress attempted to join the latter group, "she had the satisfaction of ringing the front-door bell and drinking tea in the drawing-room; but ... in a very few minutes she was out in the servants' hall", saying that the lady of the house "gave me my tea first".[16]

As previously noted in Chapter Two, the Hon Mrs John Dundas suggested that, if district nurses were supervised by ladies of their own class, "who would visit them on equal terms", they need not fear "losing caste by undertaking such work". However, any lady who worked, either from choice or necessity, could expect to lose touch with both male and female friends from her leisured days. She would probably be separated from them geographically, and had neither the money nor the time to pursue a cultural life of church meetings, tea parties and concerts.[17]

Furthermore, Stocks queries whether the early Queen's Nurses had all been 'ladies', and QVJI's unique records offer the opportunity to consider this point. As each nurse qualified as a QN, her name and details were entered on the Queen's Roll. This records date of birth, marital status, religious denomination, education, father's occupation, own previous occupation, hospital training and nursing experience, district training, certificates and badges, and reports on each post held as a QN. As we have seen, Florence Nightingale believed that, to fulfil her dual aims of curative care and preventative education, a district nurse needed to be an educated lady. Florence Craven boasted that some of the earliest applicants to train with the Metropolitan Nursing Association had been presented at Court as debutantes. However, surviving records of paternal occupations amongst the 539 nurses listed on the Queen's Roll in 1896 include several clergymen, an Oxford Professor, a solicitor, a bank manager, two army officers and a farmer, suggesting a predominantly middle-class background which, whilst not wholly leisured, would still have provided the time and income for a social life.[18]

Amongst the earliest QNs who worked in Gloucestershire, Alpha Fenton, who qualified in 1892 and worked at Charlton Kings from 1893 to 1909, was the daughter of an auctioneer and listed her own previous occupation as "housekeeper to brothers". The records of Leah Garratt, who qualified in 1890 and worked at Gotherington from 1892 to '93, do not include her father's occupation, but Leah remained "at home" until she began her hospital training at Worcester in 1886 at the age of twenty-one, which, again, suggests a comfortable background.[19]

This trend continued in the early years of the twentieth century. Of a sample of 12 nurses who qualified as QNs between 1902 and 1908, only 2 (17%) record a previous occupation: Alexina Cowee (Minchinhampton 1909-13; Badminton 1913-17) and Ann Newdick (Charlton Kings 1909-33), both of whom had been children's nurses and were the daughters of farmers. The other ten (83%) either give no previous occupation or are listed as "at home". Where father's occupation is recorded, these include a printer, a merchant and two clergymen. The father of Olive Goddard (Upton St Leonards 1907-11) was "In Her Late Majesty's consular service in China", whilst Margaret Powell (Gotherington 1904-8), the daughter of an army officer, was recorded as being "refined and nice in her ideas though not a lady by birth". The average age of commencing hospital training was 22.8 years, and training lasted for two to four years, depending on the hospital. Five of the nurses (42%) then immediately began their training as district nurses, whilst the other seven (58%) worked as private nurses or as staff nurses and sisters in hospitals and nursing homes before commencing their training, making the average age of qualifying as a QN 29.6 years.[20]

By 1913, one of the items for discussion at a Conference of Superintendents was: "It seems that the type of woman now taking up district work is not what it used to be, judging from those applying. ... Can anything be done to make this work more attractive to the woman wishing to devote herself to work amongst the sick poor?" Any points raised or conclusions reached were not recorded, but amongst QNs who qualified between 1910 and 1917, 43% had worked prior to hospital training, their occupations including a cashier and a flosser. Paternal occupations included an engineer, two bootmakers, a florist and a grocer, which suggests a more upper working-class than lower middle-class background. The average age of commencing hospital training had risen slightly to 23.7 years, but the percentage of nurses subsequently working as private and hospital nurses before starting their district training remained little changed at 57%, and the average age of qualifying as a QN was 29 years.[21]

When the question of the nurses' social background was discussed again in 1922, it was

> thought that nurses did not apply as they formerly did because there were now many more professions open to women, district work was hard, the nurses objected to further training after the three years in hospital, ... the thought of another examination and the binding of a year's agreement were deterrents, as also was the knowledge that there was no pension after the term of service.

Amongst QNs working in Gloucestershire from 1919-25, the average age of commencing hospital training had risen to 24.2 years, and with the standard three years training now required of all nurses by the Registration Act of 1919, and 67% of the nurses then gaining private and hospital experience before their district training, the average age of subsequently qualifying as a QN had risen to 32.2 years. Paternal occupations now included two engineers, a postman and a master joiner, and 67% of the nurses had previously worked, their occupations including shop assistants and a clerk. It is particularly interesting to note that, in 1907, one of the candidates selected for training as a Village Nurse-Midwife in Gloucestershire was Alice O'Brian, a servant, whilst fifteen years later, Susie Bayliss, a former serving maid, was considered suitable as a Queen's Nurse. Social background alone is, of course, no definite indicator of intelligence and practical nursing ability: Bayliss, an artisan's daughter who worked at Prestbury from 1924 to 1930, was described as "a most capable, practical nurse" and she rose to become Assistant Superintendent in Portsmouth from 1930 to 1937.[22]

All candidates for training as QNs had to have already qualified as hospital nurses though, before the Registration Act, the length and quality of their training varied. Leah Garratt trained at the General Infirmary,

Worcester, for 16 months from January 1886 to May 1887, whilst Alpha Fenton spent six months at St Barts in 1890 and six months at Bristol General Hospital in 1891. When Agnes Hunt took the examination at the end of her training as a Lady Pupil at the Salop Infirmary in 1891, she recalls, "I was not in the least afraid of not being able to pass the examination because at that time everyone passed, unless they were mentally deficient". From her memoirs, it is clear that Agnes was an intelligent though self-effacing woman, but it is true that hospital syllabuses in the late nineteenth century were limited in their scope. Nevertheless, the requirement of a prior hospital qualification, together with the breadth and depth of technical and theoretical knowledge demanded by the district training, assumed a certain level of ability and literacy. However, the Queen's Roll suggests that some candidates struggled to achieve the required standard.[23]

From its formation, QVJI emphasised that

> the subjects *not* taught to nurses in hospital ... should figure in a district nurse's training. They were sanitary reform, teaching health matters, ventilation, drainage, water supply, diets for the healthy and the sick, the feeding of infants, infectious diseases, monthly nursing of the lying-in woman [and] the care of newborn infants.

All these subjects had to be covered in the six months' training course, as well as practical work. The examination paper for QNs carried 60 marks, and although the minimum pass mark and pass rate are not known, it is clear from recorded examination results that high standards were demanded. Comments were recorded on any mark below 75%, with educational difficulties being particularly cited for working class candidates (see Table 4.1). Beatrice Price (Stone 1920-38), a grocer's daughter from Nailsworth, was noted throughout her career to be "not a good record keeper" whose "ante-natal records suggest paperwork is rather difficult".[24]

The midwifery training necessary for a rural post was equally demanding. In 1872, Florence Nightingale wrote in her *Notes on Lying-in Institutions and a Scheme for Training Midwives* that, if a midwife was to "undertake *all* cases of parturition, normal and abnormal," then she needed a "scientific and practical ... training [which] could not be given in less than two years". However, it was not until 1937 that a training period of twenty-four months was set for midwives, and even then it was only for untrained women, whilst trained nurses could complete the course in twelve months. Under the Midwives Act of 1902, the examination of the London Obstetrical Society (LOS) was replaced by a similar examination

Table 4.1 Results of the Examination for the Roll of Queen's Nurses

Year	Nurse's surname	Mark out of 60	%	Comments
1908	Newdick	42	70	Many parts good considering apparent educational difficulty.
1908	Sproat	46	76.7	Not very energetic.
1910	Lee	47	78	Some parts very good.
1910	Milford	54	90	Very good.
1911	Douglas	39½	65.8	Question 3 surprisingly poorly answered by this candidate.
1911	Tatton	41½	69	Some parts fairly good, limited abilities.
1911	Griffiths	44½	74	A good nurse but lacks finish.
1912	Paling	35	58	Handicapped by limited abilities and education.
1917	Price	38	63	Scanty, too sketchy.
1919	Boston	49	81.7	Not good at clerical work.
1923	Jenkins	51	85	Nervous and excitable.
1924	Webb, F.M.	34½	57.5	Is not very well educated.
1924	Webb, L.F.	33½	55.8	Lacking in education.
1924	Avery	45½	75.8	Very capable and methodical.

Source: CMAC SA/QNI/J.3

conducted by the newly-formed Central Midwives Board (CMB) and held four times a year. The subjects covered in the training course, as set out in the CMB's first *Rule Book*, 1903, included female anatomy, pregnancy and its principal complications, normal and abnormal labour, antiseptics in midwifery, obstetric emergencies, the management and feeding of infants, and the management of cases of puerperal fever. The training period for all midwives was set at only three months and the examination was partly written and partly oral. The written examination, like the paper for QNs, consisted of six questions to be completed in three hours, whilst the oral examination was of fifteen minutes' duration.[25]

Although the certificate of the LOS was still recognised and its possession automatically admitted a nurse to the new Roll of Midwives, opened by the CMB in October 1903, some of the earliest QNs to work in rural Gloucestershire also took the new examination. Alpha Fenton (Charlton Kings 1893-1909), who had passed the LOS Certificate in 1892, also gained the CMB Certificate in 1904. Similarly, Fanny Mellor (Gotherington 1903-04), who passed the LOS Certificate in February 1903, only eight months before the Midwives Roll opened, took the CMB Certificate a year later, whilst Helen Moore (Upton St Leonards 1903-07) passed the LOS Certificate in July 1903 and took the CMB Certificate just six months later. The fact that an additional certificate was not compulsory for these nurses, who were already practising QNs, suggests that they were anxious to be seen as up-to-date professionals.[26]

Social historian Jane Lewis states that the initial training period was set so short for fear of creating a shortage, and that the midwives themselves pressed for a longer period of training, believing that it would improve their professional status and make the work more popular among 'a superior class of women'. In 1916, the training period for untrained women was doubled to six months, but it remained at three months for trained nurses. This coincided with World War 1 and, consequently, a shortage of male doctors on the Home Front, many of them having volunteered for duty in the Army Medical Corps. The resulting increase in births attended by midwives continued after 1918, particularly in rural districts, and reports on maternal mortality, produced by Dame Janet Campbell of the Ministry of Health in 1923 and 1927, "emphasised the particularly fine record of the QVJI midwives, who served all of England and Wales with the exception of Wiltshire, Essex and Northumberland, attending 80,147 cases (10%) in 1924. Where they worked ... the maternal mortality rate was half the national rate."[27] This statistic does not differentiate between home deliveries by a midwife alone and difficult cases where a doctor was called in to assist. However, the thorough and demanding training of QVJI nurses ensured that they recognised such difficult cases and knew when to send for medical assistance, which fact alone could be instrumental in saving both mother and child.

In 1924, the training period for midwives was again doubled to twelve months for untrained women and six months for trained nurses. Meanwhile, QVJI's district training course for QNs remained at its original six months, whilst the prior qualification of not less than one year's experience in a general hospital or infirmary in 1890 was increased in 1906 to "not less than three years' training in approved hospitals or infirmaries".[28] Thus, QVJI specified a uniform length of training and standard of qualifications for all its nurses from 1890, twelve years before the Midwives Act and almost thirty years before the introduction of the Registration Act. In fact, the Queen's Roll was established at the very time that Florence Nightingale was battling with the Royal British Nurses' Association (RBNA) over the latter's attempt to provide a register of qualified nurses.

Founded and led by the formidable Mrs Ethel Bedford Fenwick, who had been made Matron of St Bartholomew's Hospital, London, at the age of twenty-four, the RBNA was agitating for a standard certificate of proficiency that would be awarded by an independent body of examiners rather than by the individual hospital at which a nurse had trained. The nurse would then be entitled to have her name placed on a national register of nurses. Nightingale believed that, even after thirty years of reform, nursing was still too unorganised and divergent for an official national register, and she used her considerable influence to ensure that the charter granted to the RBNA in 1893 omitted the word 'register' and conferred only the right to the "maintenance of a list of persons who may have applied to have their names entered thereon as nurses".[29]

Woodham-Smith stresses that Nightingale

> was not necessarily against registration, but she was passionately opposed to the kind of registration proposed. The qualifying of a nurse by examination only took no account of the character training which she held to be as important as the acquisition of technical skill. ... Nor in her opinion would the register as proposed protect the public. The fact that a nurse's name was on it would only mean that at a certain date she had satisfied the examiners in certain tests; it would tell nothing of her subsequent record. If a register were to be useful it should be kept up to date, and include a description of each nurse's character.[30]

Such a scheme was never achieved for general nurses, but from its inception, QVJI, with its national system of supervision and regular inspections, did ensure that, once qualified, its district nurses continued to maintain standards, and its centrally held records provided exactly the type of comments that Nightingale deemed essential, covering character and conduct as well as work.

Comments could be blunt and unequivocal: Caroline Lee (Gloucestershire Assistant County Superintendent 1912-14) was "hot-tempered, ... self-opinionated and impatient of control" and Susannah Jenkins (Nailsworth 1923-4) was "quick-tempered, ... very difficult and over-bearing in manner". Improvements were acknowledged as a nurse's career progressed and she became more experienced and competent: Margaret Powell (Gotherington 1904-8) was "not up to Queen's standard" in 1906, but by the time she resigned from QVJI during World War 1, to take up a post as Lady Superintendent in a munitions factory, she was reported to be "an excellent School Nurse and a willing worker". Kate Hastings from Limerick, who worked at Gotherington from 1908 to '09, was reported to be "'rough and ready' in manner" and "not competent to teach" early in her career, but when she resigned her post in Manchester to be married in 1912, her final inspection found her to be "a very capable nurse with a good educational influence".[31]

However, there was no hesitation in detailing the problems of those who failed to improve or who let standards slip. Elizabeth Williams, a Works Manager's daughter from Northampton, who qualified as a QN in January 1907, left the Cheltenham DNA in July of the same year, after her first inspection found that it was "not desirable that Nurse Williams should be recommended again". Hilda Boston (Staverton 1920-36) was noted in 1924 to be "needing supervision" as her work was "rather slipshod". Eventually she resigned from QVJI when she was "cited to appear before CMB", her final inspection having found her to be "apt to neglect details. Very impulsive and has a difficult manner." The Webb sisters (Cinderford 1924-6) were recognised as being kind and hardworking, and were liked by their patients, but Florence was considered "unsuitable for Public Health Work" and Lilian was "an unsatisfactory worker who needs strict supervision. Entirely unsuited for district midwifery and Child Welfare work."[32]

At the other extreme, an outstanding few progressed to senior positions within QVJI. Bessie Taylor, a minister's daughter from Liverpool, who worked at Gotherington from 1910 to '11, was recognised during her district training to be "suitable for responsible post". By 1920 she was County Superintendent of the West Riding, where she proved "equal to the work expected of her". Lena Milford, a bootmaker's daughter from Smethwick, enjoyed an exemplary career in Gloucestershire as Nurse at Coln St Aldwyn, Assistant County Superintendent and, from 1917 to 1946, "a wise, progressive, hard-working and highly esteemed" County

Superintendent. With her forceful personality, Caroline Lee, an engineer's daughter from Woolwich, progressed to being County Superintendent in Kent, Derbyshire and Northants, and she ended her career as a recruitment officer, presenting "Queen's Institute Propaganda in Hospitals", where she was considered to be "an excellent speaker".[33]

The Queen's Roll offers a fascinating insight into the social background and training of QNs, their characters and careers. Lewis believes that midwifery and nursing both became middle-class preserves as the twentieth century progressed. However, the evidence provided by the Queen's Roll suggests that district nursing, which combined midwifery and nursing, particularly in rural areas, increasingly attracted more young women from the upper working-classes. Furthermore, the statistic that Lewis quotes, of 10% home deliveries in 1924, refers to all QVJI nurses; it does not differentiate between Queen's Nurses and Village Nurse-Midwives who were purposely selected from amongst local working-class women.[34]

Training of Village Nurse-Midwives

Rosalind Paget pointed out that, in 1916, of the 1,375 Queen's Nurses in England, only 182 (13.2%) were practising midwifery. The need to hold a midwifery certificate, both for employment in rural districts and for promotion to posts as a Superintendent or Inspector, had been recognised by QVJI since its formation. Therefore, this statistic suggested that "very considerable value is placed on the *possession of the certificate* of the Central Midwives Board as an extra qualification to the nurse's certificate, enabling superior posts to be obtained". Paget felt that the Institute "ought to be able to depend on every Queen's Nurse who holds the CMB certificate" to realise that "they have some measure of obligation in regard to this branch of their profession", otherwise by using the certificate only as a means to obtain promotion, "they have taken the privileges without the responsibilities". It was those very responsibilities that were cited as the reason that "trained nurses, as a rule, objected to doing midwifery", when the problem was further discussed at the Annual Conference of Superintendents in 1922. It was again stated as an accepted fact that "the object of the nurses in taking the CMB examination was to enable them to obtain promotion", as each nurse "dreaded the responsibility which she must necessarily take when acting as a midwife". It was pointed out that "the nurses liked the work when once they had overcome the nervousness they naturally felt at first" and it was suggested that, as an incentive, "there should be a greater difference in the salaries offered to Queen's Nurses who were also practising midwifery". At that date, an additional £5 per annum was paid, "but if £20 were offered it would be more fair, considering all that midwifery entailed". However, one speaker reminded the Conference that in many districts the Committees lacked sufficient funds even to engage a Queen's Nurse, let alone pay her an additional £20 per annum; the problem was not, therefore, how to persuade Queen's Nurses to practise midwifery, "the question was how to raise the status of the village nurse". It was suggested that

> when interviewing applicants it was only fair to try and urge those who were young and otherwise suitable to enter hospital for their general training. This was always a difficulty, as a good many wanted to start work at once, as they could not afford to do without the salary they would earn; and of course, if such advice were followed out, good material was lost to the training homes. There were again others, older perhaps, who either were widows with young children, or with other home ties, or who were from other reasons unsuitable for hospital training.[35]

In Gloucestershire, the first report of the County Nursing Association, dated 1905, specified that the qualifications for Village Nurse-Midwives should be: "Twelve months' - or in no case under six months' - training at some approved training place, with Midwifery instruction and certificate." Unlike Queen's Nurses, who paid for their own training, the district and midwifery training of VNMs was paid for by the CNA, in return for which they contracted to work in the county for a minimum of three years. In 1906, the Gloucestershire CNA stressed that the training of VNMs "forms one of the most important duties of the Association" but this work had been "a good deal handicapped by lack of funds and the difficulty of finding suitable women to train as Village Nurses". In fact, in April 1906, when the sub-committee responsible for selecting trainees "met at the Superintendent's house to interview candidates for training as Village Nurses, only one kept her appointment and she was not considered suitable". Only two VNMs had completed their training that year and had been appointed to DNAs within the county, Mathilda Brown who "had started work at Sapperton & Coates and was much liked" and Jennie Chambers who was reported to be "doing well at Whitminster". One trainee, Rose Gardiner, had broken down in health after three months training and had been sent home, and Miss Kendall of Nailsworth, who had been interviewed and approved, regretted that "owing to private reasons" she could not accept the offer of training. A further two women,

Mrs Shaw and Letitia Burden, were in the course of training, whilst two candidates, Mrs Roberts and Mrs Till, had both twice failed to pass the CMB examination.[36]

In 1906, QVJI increased the minimum training period for VNMs from six to nine months and the cost of training each VNM was cited in 1907 as "£37.10s.0d. for a nine months' course" in general nursing and midwifery. In 1909, a QVJI Inspector was obliged to remind the Gloucestershire CNA in her annual report of "the desirability of a twelve months' training for the County Nurses, as is now generally the rule" and as was laid down in the county's own scheme. Implementation of this rule further increased the cost of training to £60 for each nurse, which expense had to be met from already stretched county funds, raised from grants, donations, subscriptions and DNA affiliation fees, supplemented by parish collections, plant and garden sales, flag days and bazaars.[37]

Between 1905 and 1919, the majority of Gloucestershire VNMs received their training at the District Nurses' Home at Plaistow in London, with the occasional placement of one or two trainees at the Victoria Home, Cheltenham, at Kingswood in Bristol or at Tipton in the West Midlands. During that period, an average of six VNMs were trained each year, "not only to supply them for newly-founded Districts, but also to replace those who continually resign their posts for various incontrovertible reasons" (see Chapter Five). From 1919, Kingswood District Nurses' Home became the main training centre for the county, although one or two trainees continued to be placed in Cheltenham. This arrangement "proved very satisfactory - the Home is very comfortable, and the pupils are thoroughly well trained and cared for in every way".[38]

In 1907, the ideal VNM was described as a "young married woman who would be able to undertake the work in her own and neighbouring parishes". This, of course, was exactly the type of woman that Elizabeth Malleson had originally suggested when she founded the Village Nursing Association (see Chapter Two). Such candidates had proved difficult to find in the 1880s, and twenty-five years later, the situation remained unchanged, with the Gloucestershire CNA reports regularly expressing regret and concern at the great scarcity of suitable candidates for training. Unfortunately, few personal details were recorded of the VNM applicants, but from the available data it can be seen that the average age of candidates accepted for training was 31.3 years (see Table 4.2). When a year is added for training, then the average age of qualifying as a VNM becomes 32.3 years. Of the seven applicants for whom marital status was recorded, one was single, one was separated, two were married and three were widows. A further twenty-one applicants (not all of whom were accepted) are referred to in the CNA Minutes as 'Mrs' but whether they were married or widowed is not recorded.[39]

Table 4.2 Applicants accepted for training as Village Nurse-Midwives

Year	Nurse's name	Background	Age
1905	Mrs Till	Wife of a coachman	
1905	Jennie Chambers		38
1906	Letitia Burden	Separated, 1 child	26
1907	Alice O'Brian	Servant	
1908	Florence Bishop	Widow, no children	30
1908	Mrs Dawe	Widow, 3 children	39
1908	Bessie Mourton	Single	35
1908	Mrs Williams	Married, 2 children	35
1912	Chapman		26
1912	Florence Mann		27
1913	Taylor		24
1913	Vallender		33
1916	Mrs Fitzgerald	Widow, 2 children (1 delicate)	

Source: GRO D2410 Minutes of Gloucestershire County Nursing Association

Amongst the earliest applicants to be rejected was Mrs Lucas of Oldbury-on-Severn, who "was 60 with no education and it was decided that it was impossible to help her", whilst Mrs Edith Mills, aged forty-four, of Painswick, was considered "too old" and Mrs Phillips of Whitminster "was quite of the cottage class". Alice Brown was rejected in 1909 "as her medical certificate stated that her heart was not quite normal"; the following year, it was decided not to train Miss A. Hathaway "as the doctor did not consider she was strong enough for district work"; and in 1911 Lizzie Hardwick was rejected "as her medical certificate was not satisfactory". Several women were classified as "unsatisfactory" or "not suitable" without any specific reason being given: Mrs Baxter, a widow from Cheltenham with six years experience as an unqualified midwife; Mrs Key of Tewkesbury; Mrs Cook of Hardwicke; Mrs Green of Blakeney Hill; and Mrs Trigg, who had been approved in 1910, but "as further information had been received ... it had been decided not to train [her]".[40]

Amongst those who were approved for training, Minnie Bishop "wrote to say she did not wish to be trained as she could not bind herself to work in the County for three years"; Bessie Mourton of Upton St Leonards and Mathilda Wardle both fell ill and could not take up their training places; whilst Mrs Loveday of Fairford and Mrs Laver of Lighthill near Stroud both decided not to be trained. Nurse Thompson did complete her training in 1907 but her work at St Briavels "was reported not to be very satisfactory". It was decided that Miss Olphert, the County Superintendent, "should talk to her and that she should be given another chance". She was transferred to a new district at Frampton in January 1908, but after just two months in her new post, the Secretary "wrote saying she had given Nurse Thompson notice as her work was not satisfactory. It was decided not to give her further employment." Fanny Wickenden was sent for training in August 1909, but she "did not appear equal to the demands made on her during the training and was recalled" in December. In that same year, another of Gloucestershire's trainee VNMs, Mrs Dawe, failed the CMB examination. The CNA Committee had clearly made a great effort to help Mrs Dawe, a thirty-nine year old widow, as sufficient money had been subscribed to keep her three children for four months and "it was decided that if she was doing well in her training, steps would be taken for the other five months". However, the Matron at the training Home "did not give a good account of her capabilities ... [and] came to the conclusion she would have much to learn before she could pass an examination. The Committee decided not to continue Mrs Dawe's training as they did not think she had the necessary qualities to make a good Village Nurse."[41]

The VNMs were expected to pass the CMB examination, i.e. the same midwifery qualification as QNs, who were already trained nurses. As we have seen, many QN candidates lacked the level of literacy this required, and the working-class VNM trainees encountered the same difficulties. This clearly caused a national problem, as in 1909, at a meeting of CNA representatives at QVJI's London offices, one of the subjects discussed was the need to simplify "the technical terms employed in the CMB examination". In 1906, Margaret Loane wrote a textbook, *Simple Introductory Lessons in Midwifery*, explaining medical terms. In the same year, the Gloucestershire CNA Committee agreed that Mrs Shaw, in training at Plaistow, would have "6d per week sent to her for books, etc.", and in 1907 the County Superintendent was authorised "to spend a sum of between 20/- and 30/- on books to be lent to pupils in training". Despite such help, candidates continued to struggle and there are frequent references in the CNA Minutes to nurses having to repeat the CMB examination. Nurse Conry managed to pass the written paper in June 1910, but failed the oral examination, which she then passed at her second attempt a month later. Nurse Higgs and Nurse Harris both failed the CMB examination in August 1910, but passed in October. Similarly, Nurse Aston passed at her second attempt in January 1913, whilst Nurse Sims only passed at her third attempt in February 1913. In 1912, "Nurse Burchill training at Plaistow was reported by the Superintendent to read and write so badly that it was feared she would not be able to pass the CMB examination. It was decided she should attend a night school while at Plaistow." Other candidates failed to complete their training. Halfway through her course in 1910, Nurse Powis decided that "owing to family matters [she] did not wish to complete her training and re-paid the fees". In the same year, Nurse Corkhill left Tipton after just one day "owing to her husband's illness. As she had stated that she was a single woman the Committee decided not to allow her to return." In 1911, Pearl Loveridge "returned home from Plaistow in bad health after 7 months training", whilst Mrs Sinclair, having "left Plaistow during her training without permission, was interviewed by the Committee and promised to repay the sum spent on her".[42]

However, those who did complete their training were reported to have "all done well", and in 1910, the value of VNMs was stressed in the *Queen's Nurses Magazine*: "What they know, they know well - they are of the country, understand the people, and are happy amongst them. ... Queen's Nurses are needed in increasing numbers, ... but under the pressure of the Midwives Act, ... the village nurses are also needed for the posts they alone can fill."[43]

The necessity of balancing the technical content of the training with the calibre of candidates remained a problem, particularly as the scope of their duties increased with the expansion of Public Health Work after 1908. The outbreak of World War 1 in 1914 also affected the recruitment of trainees, as many potential candidates took up war work in various capacities. In 1915, it was recorded that "owing to the shortage of nurses it was decided to train 8 instead of 6 this year only if applicants are the widows of soldiers or sailors for whom a grant might be obtained from the Soldiers & Sailors Families Association". However, no applications were forthcoming from this source and the following year it was again noted that it was "very difficult to obtain candidates for training". In 1917, a letter written by the Duchess of Beaufort "calling attention to the need for women to train as District Nurses" was sent to all the newspapers in the county. By endorsing a similar national appeal by the President of the Hampshire CNA, the Duchess acknowledged the "splendid desire ... [of] women to serve the country by war work", but she strongly recommended that, instead of "eagerly undertaking temporary employment where little training is necessary", women should consider training as VNMs, thus "fitting themselves to do permanent service for their country ... [as] an integral part of our health organisation". The response to the original national appeal is not known, but in Gloucestershire twelve applications were received, though "some of these would not accept the conditions of training and some were not suitable but it is hoped 2 at least will be trained". Later that same year, "a letter was sent by the Secretary to all local associations asking if they could recommend candidates for training", but only two women applied.[44]

At that time, Gloucestershire VNMs were given "careful instruction" in Public Health Work by the County Superintendent as part of her supervisory duties, but at a Conference of Superintendents attended by Miss Milford in London in 1919, it was considered desirable that such instruction should become an integral part of their training, and at the Conference of Superintendents in 1922, a resolution was passed "to the effect that the period of training for Village Nurses should be extended to one and a half years, and that three months of that time should, if possible, be devoted to school work and health visiting". In Gloucestershire, an extra three months instruction in Public Health Work was added to the one year's training in 1922/3, and in 1925/6 it was decided that the county's VNMs "will now receive eighteen months training, one year in Midwifery and six months in general and Health work", and "to bind for a period of two years instead of three".[45]

In 1924/5, the Gloucestershire CNA reported that, although the number of applicants had increased, "very few of these are suitable for the work", and a breakdown in health was still the most frequently cited reason for candidates failing to complete their training: Nurse Prince at Kingswood in 1920; Nurse Markham after only a fortnight's training in 1921; Nurse Wilkins who had been at Kingswood for three months in 1923; Nurse Hepburn who spent sixteen weeks in training at the Victoria Home, Cheltenham, also in 1923; and Nurse Smallbones who broke her contract at the end of three months training in 1924, "being too nervous for the work". In 1925, it was recorded that "it has not been possible to keep the vacancies at Kingswood filled during the whole year", and the CNA expressed "regret and surprise that many more women do not feel a vocation to a life so full of human interest and personal devotion". However, in a paper delivered at the Conference of Superintendents in 1922, Miss Johnson, the County Superintendent for the Isle of Wight, pointed out that, with the implementation of the Registration Act, "the most eminently suitable women would consider the county training not worth while" because, on the completion of her training, each candidate "will not be a fully qualified nurse ... [and] she will be unable to come into any scheme for the benefit of fully trained nurses". In Gloucestershire, attempts were made to recognise the quality and professionalism of the VNMs by the introduction, in 1919, of a certificate "for nurses leaving the County after fulfilling their contract and having worked satisfactorily", and in 1920, by the wearing of a county badge: a white enamelled badge during a VNM's first two years of service, then "if satisfactory", a red badge.[46]

Despite such ongoing problems and concerns, VNMs remained invaluable. In England and Wales as a whole, they represented 25.44% of QVJI nurses in 1905; by 1925, this figure had risen to 62.38%, a percentage increase of 36.94. In Gloucestershire, a predominantly rural county, VNMs as a proportion of QVJI nurses rose from 57.14% in 1907 to 82.44% in 1925. In a report dated 1926, but using data from 1925, the County Medical Officer of Health described how

> much useful work has been done by the District Nurses in the County and the value of their services as health agencies in the homes becomes more obvious as time goes on. It is scarcely stating too much to say that there is no other service which has such full opportunity for promoting the general health of the country, for the home is the unit of health work, and the District Nurse enters it more intimately than can any other health official.

In addition to their routine district work, the county nurses were also involved with:

1. Nursing work in connection with the Public Elementary Schools.
2. Visiting cases of Tuberculosis.
3. Health Visiting in connection with the scheme for Maternity & Child Welfare, including visits to homes of infants with measles, etc.
4. Care of mentally defective and boarded-out children.

Throughout the report, the need for discretion, tact and confidentiality are emphasised, and the scope of the scheme illustrates how the VNMs were expected to carry the same weight of responsibility as Queen's Nurses, "thus making them", in the words of Miss Johnson, "more useful and valuable members of the profession which barely owns them".[47]

Although professional resentment persisted nationally, in Gloucestershire the dual system of Queen's Nurses and Village Nurse-Midwives, both combining district nursing with midwifery and health work, was clearly a success, and in its report of 1925/6, the Gloucestershire CNA recorded with pride that "the combination of State and Voluntary Work as carried out in this County is held up as a model all over the Country". Furthermore, the nurses, both QNs and VNMs, enjoyed a great sense of professional satisfaction and social status through their close contact with their patients. In late nineteenth and early twentieth century hospitals, all patients were referred to by their bed number, and nurses were frequently changed from side to side in a ward, to prevent them getting to know any patient too well. It was also traditional to call senior nurses by the names of their wards (e.g. Sister Clinical) instead of by their own surnames. In contrast to such an impersonal atmosphere, rural district nursing offered the opportunity to befriend entire families and to occupy a position of trust and respect within the community.[48]

Amongst the QNs who served in Gloucestershire, where the rural movement began, Alpha Fenton worked at Charlton Kings for seventeen years and her successor, Ann Newdick, for twenty-four years; Rose Paling worked at Lydney for sixteen years, Beatrice Price at Stone for eighteen years, and Lucy Avery at Nailsworth for twenty-four years. Amongst the longest-serving VNMs in the county, Nurse Shaw started work at Avening in 1907; Florence Cooper at Tidenham in 1909; Mabel Judd transferred to Painswick in 1913 after four years at North Nibley; Nurse Kite was appointed to Blakeney & Awre in 1911; Alice Hunt to Stanton in 1911; Nurse Self to Horton in 1912; and Nurse Fitzgerald transferred to Wickwar in 1919, after three years at Hawkesbury Upton: all were still in the same posts in 1925. Four of these long-serving VNMs (Shaw, Kite, Self and Fitzgerald) were already either married or widowed when they began their training, whilst two of the longest serving QNs remained in their posts after marriage, Beatrice Price becoming Mrs Pullir in 1927 and Lucy Avery becoming Mrs Abbotts in 1936. VNM Nurse Bridges, who worked for the CEHQS DNA from 1917 to 1927, was allowed to continue in her post when she became Mrs Day in 1922, when she informed the Committee that "she would like to settle down in Southrop". Similarly, VNMs Nurse Hill, appointed to Kings Stanley in 1919, and Nurse Cooper, appointed to Wotton-under-Edge in the same year, remained in the same posts when they both married in 1925, becoming Mrs Miles and Mrs Witchell respectively. This, of course, was in marked contrast to hospital nurses, who were expected to resign on marriage, and it must have been an inducement to those who wished to combine a family life with paid service to the community of which they had become an integral part.[49]

At Upton St Leonards in 1908, the County Superintendent reported that Nurse Olive Goddard "is loved by her patients ... [and] it was a pleasure to go round the district with her", whilst at Gotherington in 1911, Elizabeth Malleson noted that "Nurse Griffiths has already won her place amongst us by her habitual manner of regarding patients not only as 'cases' in nursing parlance, but as neighbours and friends requiring her skilled help". Alexina Cowee (Minchinhampton 1909-13, Badminton 1913-17) was "a kind, unselfish and attentive nurse. Much liked." Lily Tatton (Nailsworth 1914-16) was "conscientious and hard-working, kind and with a gentle manner", and Lucy Avery (Nailsworth 1924-48) was "a keen and energetic nurse, much appreciated by doctors and patients". When the Painswick Charities Trustees formed a new sub-committee in 1917 "for the benefit of the sick in this district", they elected Nurse Judd as a member to advise and assist in the allocation of funds, in recognition of her judgment and knowledge of the poor in their community. At Nailsworth in 1920, it was recorded that "the Nurse is welcomed everywhere", and by 1924, the Gloucestershire CNA was "particularly glad to be able to report that ... the desire to have a Nurse in practically every parish comes from the people themselves, and is a gratifying proof that the quiet devoted work of the Nurses in the homes for the past twenty years and more is bearing fruit".[50]

The appreciation felt by the poor was often displayed by simple but touching gestures. One of QVJI's most stringent rules was that "the nurse shall not accept any presents from patients or their friends", but at Upton St Leonards in 1907, the DNA Committee found it necessary to modify this rule by the addition of the clause "other than flowers or fruit". At Gotherington in 1913, Elizabeth Malleson recorded that, "one suffering woman on her death-bed begged that the Nurse might be asked to accept the gift of one of her possessions as a token of her care and help; such a gift was against official rules, but in my mind such a wish left no obligation but obedience to it." The DNA Committee at Nailsworth was also willing to interpret the rule flexibly, as it was noted in 1925 that Nurse Avery "frequently tells the Committee members that on her return home from work she finds on her doorstep gifts of a few plants, flowers, a few eggs, a pot of jam, and similar marks of gratitude from an appreciative public."[51]

The work of rural district nurses demanded skill, tact and stamina. They suffered initial opposition from the medical profession, and financial and social deprivation. However, those nurses who proved suitable for rural district work derived a great sense of satisfaction from their combined duties of nursing, midwifery and Public Health Work. Whether single, married or widowed, they could live as part of a community in which they were valued, trusted and respected, not only as a skilled professional, but also as a friend and neighbour. In return, they were rewarded with the hard-won respect, affection and gratitude of their poor patients.

Notes

1. *The Lancet*, 20 Dec 1879, 919.
   M. Jeanne Peterson, 'The Victorian Governess: Status Incongruence in Family and Society' in *Suffer and Be Still*, ed. by Martha Vicinus (London: Methuen, 1972), pp.3-19.
   Pamela Horn, *The Rise & Fall of theVictorian Servant*, (Stroud: Sutton, 1990), pp.67 & 201.
   Martha Vicinus, *Independent Women: Work & Community for Single Women 1850-1920* (London: Virago, 1985), p.113.
2. Robert Dingwall, Anne Marie Rafferty & Charles Webster, *An Introduction to the Social History of Nursing* (London: Routledge, 1988), p.182.
   Virginia Berridge, 'Health & Medicine' in *The Cambridge Social History of Britain 1750-1950: Vol 3 Social Agencies & Institutions*, ed. by F.M.L. Thompson (Cambridge University Press, 1990), pp.171-242.
   Rosemary White, *Social Change & the Development of the Nursing Profession* (London: Kimpton, 1978), p.55.
3. Cited by Judith Moore, *A Zeal for Responsibility: The Struggle for Professional Nursing in Victorian England, 1868-1883* (University of Georgia, 1988), p.41.
4. Dr W.M. Banks, letter to *The British Medical Journal*, Vol 2, 1896, p.43.
   Mary Stocks, *A Hundred Years of District Nursing* (London: Allen & Unwin, 1960), p.77.
   Brian Abel-Smith, *A History of the Nursing Profession* (London: Heinemann, 1960), p.75.
   Dr Alex McCook Weir, letter to *The British Medical Journal*, Vol 2, 1896, p.1523.
   Dr Robert Rentoul, cited by Jean Donnison, *Midwives & Medical Men: A History of Inter-Professional Rivalries & Women's Rights* (New York: Schocken Books, 1977), p.121.
5. Betty Cowell & David Wainwright, *Behind the Blue Door: The History of the Royal College of Midwives, 1881-1981* (London: Bailliere Tindall, 1981), pp.26-28.
6. GRO D4057/14 Gotherington album of documents re formation of the RNA 1884-94.
   Hope Malleson, *Elizabeth Malleson: A Memoir* (Printed for Private Circulation, 1926), p.145.
   GRO D4057/15 Gotherington DNA Annual Reports 1890-1916.
7. GRO D4057/1 Gloucestershire CNA Annual Reports 1905-65.
   GRO D4057/3 Glos CNA Correspondence 1910-11.
8. GRO P244a MI 13/1 Painswick DNA Minutes 1900-20.
9. GRO D4057/3.
   GRO P347 MI 3/1 Upton St Leonards DNA Minutes 1901-09.

10. GRO D4057/3.
11. GRO P244a MI 13/1.
12. Rosalind Paget, 'The Midwife Question & Queen's Nurses', *Queen's Nurses' Magazine*, Vol XV Part 2 (1918), 27-29.
    Monica Baly, *A History of the Queen's Nursing Institute* (Beckenham: Croom Helm, 1987), p.38.
    Dr Alex McCook Weir, letter to *The British Medical Journal*, Vol 2, 1896, p.1523.
13. GRO D4057/1.
    Some Queen's Superintendents, *Handbook for Queen's Nurses* (London: Scientific Press, 1924), p.30.
14. CMAC Records of Queen's Nurses SA/QNI/J.3/10, J.3/18, J.3/19 & J.3/23.
15. Horn, *Victorian Servant*, p.33.
    Donnison, *Midwives & Medical Men*, p.141.
    GRO D3548 6/1 Bundle of 9 miscellaneous documents 1896-1928.
    Agnes Hunt, *Reminiscences* (Shrewsbury: Wilding, 1935), pp.81-2.
16. Unattributed, 'County Nursing Associations & Their Work', *Queen's Nurses' Magazine*, Vol VII Part 1 (April 1910), 9-11.
    GRO D4057/1.
    Coln St Aldwyn, Eastleach, Hatherop, Quenington & Southrop DNA Annual Reports 1911-25, Hicks-Beach private family papers.
    Flora Thompson, *Lark Rise to Candleford* (Harmondsworth: Penguin, 1973 edition, first published 1939-43), pp.196-7.
17. Letter to *The Times*, 26 Sept 1889, p.7, c.6.
    Peterson, 'Victorian Governess', p.13.
    Vicinus, *Independent Women*, p.117.
18. Stocks, *District Nursing*, p.89.
19. CMAC SA/QNI/J.3/2.
20. CMAC SA/QNI/J.3/9-15.
21. Unattributed, 'The Conference of Queen's Superintendents', *Queen's Nurses Magazine*, Vol X Part 2, (April 1913), 35-37.
    CMAC SA/QNI/J.3/17-23.
22. Unattributed, 'Report of Queen's Superintendents' Annual Conference', *Queen's Nurses Magazine*, Vol XIX Part 2 (1922), 25-29.
    CMAC SA/QNI/J.3/24-31.
    GRO D2410 Minutes of Glos CNA, 1904-1928.
    CMAC SA/QNI/J.3/28.
23. CMAC SA/QNI/J.3/2.
    Hunt, *Reminiscences*, pp.73-4.
24. Baly, *Queen's Nursing Institute*, p.37.
    CMAC SA/QNI/J.3/23.

25. Jean Towler & Joan Bramall, *Midwives in History & Society*, (London: Croom Helm, 1986), pp.158 & 180-3.
26. CMAC SA/QNI/J.3/2, J.3/9 & J.3/10.
27. Jane Lewis, *The Politics of Motherhood: Child & Maternal Welfare in England, 1900-1939* (London: Croom Helm, 1980), pp.121, 142 & 144.
28. GRO D2410.
29. Carrie Howse, 'Registration: A Minor Victory?', *Nursing Times*, Vol 85 No 49 (December 6-12 1989), 32-4.
30. Cecil Woodham-Smith, *Florence Nightingale* (London: Book Club Associates, 1972 edition, first published 1950), pp.571-3.
31. CMAC SA/QNI/J.3/10, J.3/13, J.3/17 & J.3/29.
32. CMAC/SA/QNI/J.3/13, J.3/24 & J.3/30.
33. CMAC SA/QNI/J.3/15 & J.3/17.
34. Lewis, *Politics of Motherhood*, p.145.
35. *QNM*, Vol XV Part 2 (1918), 27.
    QNM, Vol XIX Part 2 (1922), 25-29.
36. GRO D4057/1.
    GRO D2410.
37. GRO D4057/1.
38. Ibid.
39. Ibid.
    GRO D2410.
40. Ibid.
41. Ibid.
42. GRO D4057/1.
    GRO D2410.
43. GRO D4057/1.
    QNM, Vol VII Part 1 (April 1910), 10.
44. GRO D2410.
    Gloucestershire Echo, 9 April 1917, p.4, c.6.
45. GRO D2410.
    QNM, Vol XIX Part 2 (1922), 27.
    GRO D4057/1.
46. Ibid.
    GRO D2410.
    QNM, Vol XIX Part 2 (1922), 29-30.
47. Enid Fox, *District Nursing and the Work of District Nursing Associations in England & Wales, 1900-48* (PhD Thesis, London University, 1993), p.158.
    GRO D4057/1.
    GRO D4057/6 Gloucestershire County Council Co-ordination of Nursing 1926.
    QNM, Vol XIX Part 2 (1922), 30.

48. GRO D4057/1.
    Christopher J. Maggs, *The Origins of General Nursing* (Beckenham: Croom Helm, 1983), p.159.
    Vicinus, *Independent Women*, p.107.
    Moore, *Zeal for Responsibility*, p.58.
49. CMAC SA/QNI/J.3.
    GRO D4057/1.
    CEHQS DNA Minutes Book 1914-46.
50. GRO P347 MI 3/1.
    GRO D4057/15.
    CMAC SA/QNI/J.3/11, J.3/18 & J.3/31.
    GRO P244a MI 13/1.
    GRO D3548 3/1.
    GRO D4057/1.
51. GRO D4057/3.
    GRO P347 MI 3/1.
    GRO D4057/15.
    GRO D3548 3/1.

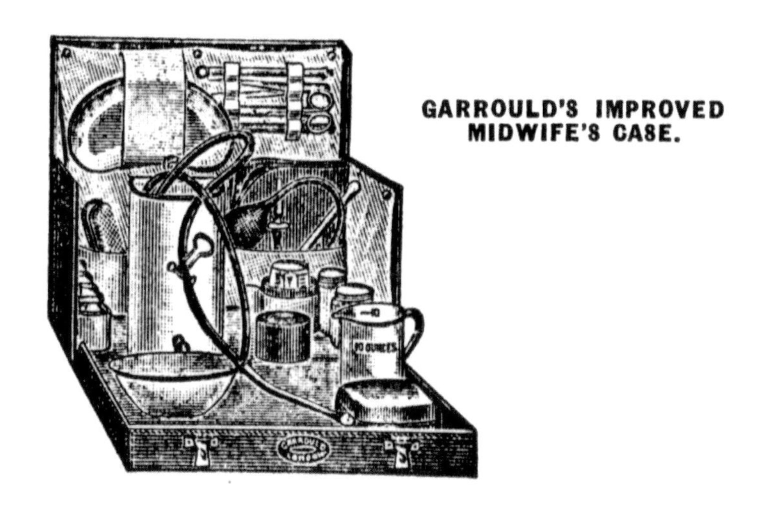

CHAPTER FIVE

THE NURSES: WORKING LIVES

Workload

In a national fund-raising and publicity pamphlet, published in 1894, Lady Victoria Lambton invites her readers to "follow one of the Queen's Nurses on part of her daily round" in the country. Our "typical Nurse", we are told, "is a fair, fresh-complexioned woman, with a pleasing voice and manner, [who] drives about her district in a little varnished two-wheeled cart with a grey pony". She sets off promptly at half-past eight in the morning and "her first patient to-day is a carter, aged about thirty-five, with a nice wife, who is busy getting her three children off to school. He is suffering from pneumonia", and having tended to him, Nurse writes out "a little time-table" to ensure that his wife "clearly understands the doctor's directions for the giving of nourishment and medicine throughout the day". Her next patients are "a mother and baby, whose home is more than a mile away, in a lonely cottage set down in the middle of fields. The woman is not a very deserving character, nor is her husband. Rolling stones! dirty and thriftless!" However, after this first visit from the Nurse, they are reformed characters; she has "won the woman's heart ... and in gratitude she promises amendment when she is about again". The Nurse "now trots her pony to another cottage, where a little boy has fallen out of a tree and has broken his leg. Poor little man! He was very sad and frightened," but when Nurse arrives, "his eyes brightened and his tears dried up". Our next visit is to "a little servant-maid, aged fifteen, sent home from her first place in the nearest town with rheumatic fever, due to sleeping in a damp bed. It is to a poor, overcrowded cottage that poor Agnes is sent home", but we find her "lying between blankets, in a room to herself, with a small fire burning, and the atmosphere sweet and wholesome", for our Nurse has "persuaded them to let Agnes have a bed to herself! and ... to open the window every morning for twenty minutes". After a homily on the benefits of fresh air, we catch Nurse up "at the almshouses, where daily she attends upon an old widow with cancer in the breast, and alleviates her pain and discomfort. No cure is possible here, only alleviation, but", Lady Victoria asks us, "is not that worth much?" After a further homily on the needs of chronic patients, we return home with the Nurse for two hours, where she can "rest herself and her pony before starting on her afternoon round".[1]

In her sentimental, almost twee style, Lady Victoria presents a sanitised, idealistic picture that is far removed from the harsh reality of rural poverty, unmade roads and changeable weather that the district nurses actually encountered. In practice, the Gloucestershire CNA admitted in its Annual Report of 1921/22, "the life of a District Nurse is an arduous and often lonely one. ... It is not easy to find fully trained Nurses who are willing to live and work in quiet out of the way country districts." In fact, when Nailsworth DNA advertised for a replacement Queen's Nurse in 1920, no replies were received.[2]

This was a problem which had been keenly felt at the Gotherington DNA since its formation. The Constitution of QVJI's Rural District Branch, dated 1892, states that "experience has shown that one nurse can efficiently nurse such a district within a radius of from three to four miles of her home, where a donkey cart is provided. ... Where a vehicle is provided ... one nurse is found sufficient for every 2,500 to 3,000 of the population." Whilst the population served by the Gotherington DNA never exceeded 2,500 up to 1925, it was what Hope Malleson described as "a particularly extended district, comprising nine villages and hamlets, so that a ... cart barely sufficed for the nurse's visits to her patients". The district covered approximately 12,500 acres, compared with Badminton DNA which covered approximately 3,000 acres with a population of less than 1,000; Nailsworth DNA, approximately 5,000 acres, population 4,000; Painswick DNA, 6,000 acres, population 2,600; and Upton St Leonards DNA, 3,000 acres, population 1,000.[3]

The Gotherington DNA Annual Reports from 1891 to 1906 show a steady workload for the district nurse (see Table 5.1). Elizabeth Malleson explains that, in the years when the number of visits decrease, "the number of maternity cases dealt with by the Queen's Nurse have increased. ... This kind of nursing occupies from its nature, so much time that the number of actual *visits* in the year are smaller." Overall, Elizabeth points out in 1891, the increase in workload "must invariably appear slight when compared with the number of visits paid by district nurses in towns. But it must always be remembered in rural nursing that the time spent in going from one part of a scattered district to another ... often equals in amount the time which is actually devoted to nursing." In 1892, she adds, "At times of pressure, the number of visits actually required of the nurse throughout the District ... have sometimes amounted to eight or more a day." During the seven months from June to December 1897, Nurse Jenny Wolfe travelled a total of 1,294 miles in her donkey cart, an average of 185 miles per month. To meet the needs of increased travelling between the different parts of the district as the nurse's workload grew, a second donkey was provided in 1892 and by 1900 a bicycle was also available. However, in 1901 Elizabeth admitted that "neither the bicycle in adverse weather, nor the donkey cart, suffices to carry her [the nurse] with

Table 5.1 Workload of Gotherington DNA, 1891-1906

Year	Number of visits	Maternity cases	Nights on duty
1891	1,196	14	Not given
1892	1,734	23	-"-
1893	2,241	21	-"-
1894		Report missing	
1895		-"-	
1896	1,428	29	-"-
1897	1,098	40	-"-
1898	1,118	30	-"-
1899		Report missing	
1900	1,733	22	31
1901	1,699	31	29
1902	2,324	32	31
1903	2,474	37	18
1904	2,404	39	22
1905	3,929	47	30
1906	5,002	52	64

Source GRO D4057/15

satisfactory speed when patients live at distances apart, and require her help at the same time". She hoped that "if a rough quiet pony could be substituted for one of the donkeys it would be very desirable, although this would mean some increase of expense". This was not achieved until 1910, when Elizabeth herself provided the necessary additional funds. In the meantime, in 1906, she reminded patients that "it is *always* expected that some vehicle should be sent for the nurse to a confinement. Summonses of this nature often come when the donkey is too tired to go further, after work, and bicycling may be impossible." It is somewhat ironic to note that, whilst concern was expressed for the donkey, the nurse was expected to respond to the summons regardless of *her* tiredness and the number of hours she had already worked.[4]

The Gloucestershire CNA Annual Report of 1906 states that "the Nurse's work shall not as a rule average more than eight hours daily, and on Sunday she will only attend urgent cases". By 1924, the Superintendents explain, "the hours of work do not, as a rule, average more than forty-four a week, one afternoon being free and serious cases only being visited on

Sunday. ... Night nursing is not usually undertaken by Queen's Nurses, but on occasion in the country it may be necessary for the nurse to stay for a night or two with a patient dangerously ill or in an emergency." The *Rules for Nurses* of QVJI's Rural District Branch also state that "Sunday & Night Duty - Are not expected from Nurses except in critical and confinement cases", but in the report of the Gotherington DNA for 1893, Elizabeth Malleson writes that "scarcely one Sunday in the twelve months has been free from visits to urgent cases, and in estimating the devotion of the nurse to her work, there must be taken into account the constant strain of anxiety it involves". Even on routine days, the nominal eight hours were expected to be highly flexible. At Staverton in 1902, it was announced that the newly arrived district nurse "will start upon her rounds every day at 9a.m. Anyone who wishes to see her about small dressings, small accidents, etc., should call by 8.30 in the morning, or 8 in the evening, when the nurse will generally be in. Of course, messages may be sent to Nurse, to go anywhere, at any time." In 1905, the building of the local railway near Gotherington brought many navvies and their families to the neighbourhood, and for one month alone during that year Nurse Margaret Powell "recorded work over 8 hours a day for 30 consecutive days, and 4 nights on duty". In Elizabeth Malleson's opinion, this was "too great a strain to continue wisely" and a VNM, Miss Jessie Trueman, "an exceptionally suitable candidate for nursing employment", was appointed to help until the completion of the railway and the consequent departure of the workers.[5]

Respiratory diseases (particularly bronchitis, pneumonia and phthisis), influenza and rheumatic fever appear regularly on surviving lists of the more serious cases nursed, as do abscesses and ulcers, burns and scalds, sprains and fractures, and "convulsions and derangements from improper feeding". The spring of 1891 saw an outbreak of scarlet fever in the Gotherington district, in which two children died; an epidemic of measles broke out in the autumn of 1892; and in 1896 and 1897 there were cases of diphtheria. There was also a major outbreak of diphtheria in Nailsworth in October 1900, when 46 cases were nursed in their own homes and 24 cases at a Temporary Isolation Hospital set up in the Infant Schoolroom.[6]

One death occurred in the number of maternity cases at Gotherington in 1891, but, Elizabeth Malleson recorded, "in the universal sorrow caused by this sad loss, it is a satisfaction to know that the two doctors in attendance on the patient, expressed their approval of the Nurse's devotion and skill, although all efforts to save life were unavailing". In 1892, "a young mother, ... having been ill before her confinement, developed serious illness after the birth of her child. ... After six weeks devoted nursing ... most happily she has been saved ... and a great deal of ... sympathy for the nursing work has been elicited in consequence of this case." In 1896, "one rare and dangerous maternity case ... was removed to the Victoria Home, Cheltenham, for operation ... [which] saved the lives of both mother and child".[7]

In 1903, Elizabeth Malleson expressed concern that "cases of acute illness often admit of no delay", to the detriment of "those suffering from the discomforts of age or incurable sickness". With the appointment of an assistant VNM in Gotherington in 1905, Nurse Powell looked "forward to being well able to give the extra needed attention to chronic patients whom she is very conscious have not received sufficient visits while more pressing cases have claimed so much of her time".[8]

It must also be remembered that in the days before antibiotic, sulphonamide and analgesic drugs, the preparations and treatments available for the nurses to use were limited. Agnes Hunt recalls her first appointment as a Queen's Nurse on the Isle of Wight in 1892, when the doctor

> asked me to help him in his dispensary. I knew nothing about dispensing, but he promised to teach me. Certainly, it did not prove to be difficult, as one prescription consisted of rhubarb and soda, and the other of quinine, iron and brown sugar. He told me to make up three gallons of each, and when the patients came I was to ask for their bottles and fill them up. He added that I could tell which they had been having because there was always a bit of sediment left in the rhubarb bottle, but if they thought the medicine was not doing them any good, I could give them some of the other. If, however, it was a new patient, it would be best to start them on the rhubarb and soda.[9]

Margaret Loane, writing in 1905, lists twelve requisite oils, ointments and powders that the nurse should carry in her bag, four of which she classified as "indispensable":

1. Methylated spirit.
2. Permanganate of potash.
3. Boracic ointment.
4. Dusting powder.

Loane urges the nurse to make her own lotions and potions instead of buying them "ready mixed from the chemist. This is extremely expensive ... to the Association ... and it is a totally unnecessary outlay, as it is perfectly simple for any nurse to buy the materials cheaply and prepare lotions of any required strength." She includes in her manual recipes for a variety of preparations, including "Poppy-head fomentation", which begins: "Get three poppy-heads from the chemist, break into small pieces and boil quickly in a quart of water for fifteen minutes." The ancient use of leeches is still recommended in a detailed and graphic section, which includes the useful directive: "The weight of the leech's body should be supported. Otherwise it may drop off from fatigue before it is satiated."[10]

By 1924, an advertisement in the Superintendents' *Handbook* promotes Germolene as the ultimate, modern aseptic dressing: "As the result of unique processes in mixing and grinding of the ingredients unrivalled homogeniety has been secured."[11]

Even when modern equipment, suitable for hospital or urban use, was available, it could prove impractical in a rural district. At the Coln St Aldwyn, Eastleach, Hatherop, Quenington & Southrop (CEHQS) DNA in 1917, it was decided to sell the sterilizer "as it is for use over gas, and a fish-kettle has been always used instead".[12]

Full and careful details of all nursing treatment and care had to be recorded in four books:

(1) Register of cases, in which was entered the personal details of the patients, their medical conditions and treatment.
(2) Daily Visiting Book, for recording the visits paid each day to each patient.
(3) Time Book, for recording the nurse's working hours.
(4) Lending Book, in which a record was kept of articles lent, to whom and when returned.

These books were regularly inspected by the Committee of the DNA, and the Superintendents stressed that "records are of great importance. ... To be of use, however, they must be complete, definite, accurate and thoroughly well kept. ... The time spent on them should not be grudged."[13]

In addition, in a leaflet issued to DNAs in 1909, QVJI, suggested that

> In the country, ... the nurse, when not busy, should be encouraged to visit any chronic cases or old people and read to or otherwise interest them, or to take charge of a young child to relieve a busy mother for an hour or two. ... As the nurse is responsible to the Committee for the good order of the various garments lent to patients, she may also, when not busy, keep them in repair.[14]

The nurses' workload was further increased by the introduction of Public Health Work. In Gotherington, Nailsworth and Painswick the nurses began assisting in the medical inspection of schoolchildren in 1909. Nurse Lane at Nailsworth attended seven schools during that year and more than 300 children were inspected, a total of 47 hours work in addition to her routine district nursing. At Badminton DNA, Nurse Alexina Cowee added School Nursing to her duties in 1914, Health Visiting in 1916 and TB Nursing in 1917. By 1916, the Gloucestershire CNA reported that, "of the 72 District Nursing Associations affiliated to the County Nursing Association 64 are co-operating in this scheme for Public Health Work".[15]

By 1917, there were also sixteen Infant Welfare Centres in the county, attended by the district nurses. At the CEHQS DNA, a weekly Baby Clinic was set up in 1915 at the Coln Reading Room for the mothers of Coln, Hatherop and Quenington, where their babies were "to be inspected and weighed etc by Nurse Jenkins. ... She will advize them as to feeding, clothing and other matters and Dr Bloxsome has kindly promised to attend at the Room one day each month. ... Several members of the Committee kindly promised either to be present and take down notes and otherwise help Nurse or to give tea to the mothers present." The following year, a weekly Baby Clinic was also set up to cover the other two villages in the DNA, held alternately in Eastleach and Southrop, where Nurse Lawrence was also Health Visitor and Tuberculosis Visitor.[16]

At Painswick in 1917, the question of Health Work was discussed by the DNA Committee, "as Nurse Judd had hinted that it was becoming too great a burden and that if it increased she would have to discontinue it". Fortunately, local doctor's wife and Committee member Mrs Robertson volunteered to help with running the Infant Welfare Centre and "filling out the forms", which arrangement proved satisfactory. In her Annual Report for the CEHQS DNA in 1919, Lucy St Aldwyn stressed that

> With the Maternity & Baby Welfare work, as well as the other branches of health visiting, and the compiling of many statistics, card-filling, etc., as required by the Local Government Board, in addition to all the daily labours of a District Nurse, there is quite enough work in the five villages to keep two Nurses fully occupied, and they rarely get a free afternoon for themselves.

In fact, the Minutes Book reveals that the CEHQS nurses had no free afternoon in any week between July 1917 and February 1918, whilst at Nailsworth in 1920, Nurse Mildred Stephens attended the local Infant Welfare Centre "each Tuesday afternoon for 1½ hours".[17]

By 1922, the number of Infant Welfare Centres in the county had increased to twenty-five, but Charlton Kings did not open its IWC until 1923. Mary Paget, whose mother Mrs Hill was one of the founder members, recalls, "Everything was run on half a shoestring - not even a whole one!" Fortnightly sessions were held in the Village Hall which, Mrs Paget remembers

> was not ideal - it had no loo, it involved stairs up which children and equipment had to be carried, and it was just one large area which had to be divided into a Doctor's corner, a Nurses' corner and a Weighing corner with one weighing machine for babies and another for toddlers. These areas had to be separated off with screens. Mothers had to undress babies in the main area and had only a few chairs on which to park their belongings.

The first session of the Charlton Kings IWC, held early in 1923, was attended by only eight mothers with eight infants. By December of that same year, there were 68 mothers and 76 infants on the books, and the Gloucestershire CNA acknowledged that "few people realize the difficulties of running rural centres. ... Nurses need encouragement and help to enable them to continue this important work."[18]

In the build-up to World War 1, the Red Cross Society requested that members of the Painswick Voluntary Aid Detachment of auxiliary nurses should be allowed to accompany the district nurse on her rounds "in order to gain instruction". Nurse Judd was willing to undertake this additional work and the Committee agreed that one lady VAD at a time would be given four weeks' training, on condition that "every lady will be completely under the orders of the Nurse ... and she undertakes to obey the Nurse in every way and not to talk about the patients or treatment to anyone. If this rule is in any way broken ... the Member will be dismissed from her Detachment." At the CEHQS DNA in 1914, "both nurses gave very useful help to the members of the Red Cross Society, who met very frequently for practice in bandaging, bed making, &c., during the summer months". At Badminton DNA in 1915, it was also noted that Nurse Cowee "helps with Red Cross". During the war, arrangements were made between the Gloucestershire CNA and the Gloucestershire War Pensions Committee "for the provision in suitable cases of nursing by the Association's nurses of soldiers and sailors discharged as unfit for further service who are recommended ... as being in want of special treatment". In 1918, during the influenza epidemic, Nurse Bridges arrived "to take over all the nursing of Eastleach and Southrop, with the outlying farm cottages. Her arrival was heartily welcomed", and throughout the county as a whole, many of the nurses "worked incessantly, day and night, and but for their devotion there would have been many more deaths".[19]

In addition to this heavy workload, the Superintendents urged each nurse to "keep herself abreast of new knowledge and developments. ... Time given to reading [and] lectures ... is time well spent." To this end, in 1917 the Gloucestershire CNA introduced "Meetings for Nurses ... of an instructive nature", which it was hoped would "be found helpful and enable the Nurses in rather isolated districts to keep in touch with new branches of work". In 1917, six such meetings were held in different parts of the county; by the following year, the number had increased to eight, with instruction being given on 'Diseases of School Children', 'Tuberculosis Nursing & Visiting', 'General Work' and 'Venereal Diseases'. In June 1919, a Course of Six Lectures to Midwives was arranged and in 1920 the theme was Health Work. In April 1922, a Nursing & Midwifery Conference was held at Shire Hall, Gloucester, organised by a Committee representing local Hospitals, Nursing Homes and the CNA. Speakers included Lady Barrett, MD, who discussed 'Danger Signals of Pregnancy', and Miss Skinner, Superintendent of the Berkshire CNA, whose address was entitled 'The Vocation of Nursing: the difficulties and opportunities of the District Nurse'. By 1923, the Conference had moved to the Guildhall, Gloucester, and took place over three days, with an average attendance of about one hundred at each of the two daily lectures. What percentage of those attending were district nurses is not known, but the Gloucestershire CNA hoped "that local Committees will realize what a great help it is to their Nurses to have the opportunity of hearing good lectures, and that they will do all in their power to enable them to attend as far as their work will allow".[20]

That final, qualifying statement illustrates the CNA's recognition of the pressure that such a workload placed on the nurses, and this was reflected by frequent changes of county personnel.

Turnover of Staff

A Queen's Nurse, on completion of her training, would be sent for one year to a post arranged by QVJI. The Superintendents warn that "it is not always possible to place her exactly where she would like to work, because there may be no vacancy in that particular part of the country" and they add that "a nurse is not expected to leave her post on the completion of her agreement, but she is then free to apply for a vacancy elsewhere". The Gloucestershire CNA, in its first report of 1905, stated that for a VNM "no training will be given unless the Candidate shall have signed an agreement to serve a Gloucestershire Association for a term of not less than 3 years after her training is completed".[21]

Such provisions were obviously designed to ensure some degree of stability and continuity, but in Gotherington by 1891 Mrs Cotterill had been replaced by Susan Stanford and by 1892, Leah Garratt had taken charge of the work. Exactly a year later, in 1893, Elizabeth Malleson reported, "Nurse Garratt felt herself obliged to leave ... but we were fortunate enough to get the temporary help of Nurse Clutterbuck until Mrs Wolfe could take charge of the work". Jenny Wolfe devoted herself to her duties, but in 1898 Elizabeth sadly recorded: "In July, Nurse Wolfe, who had been the faithful and beloved nurse of the District for over five years, was stricken with illness in the midst of her work, and died two months later, mourned by all who knew her moral rectitude and her unselfish devotion to those who needed her skill and sympathy." Two temporary nurses divided the work between them "in the most satisfactory manner" until Beatrice Priestley was engaged and took up her duties with "thoroughness and cheerfulness". However, Nurse Priestley left in 1901 and there were further changes of nurse in 1902, 1903 and 1904. When Margaret Powell arrived in November 1904, with "much love of her work and devotion to patients", Elizabeth Malleson hoped "that a long period of settlement is before us". Powell remained in her post for four years, but resigned in tragic circumstances (as described later) in the summer of 1908. Her replacement, Kate Hastings, remained for only a year and there were further changes of nurse in 1910, 1911, 1914, 1915 and 1916. In view of what has already been established concerning Elizabeth Malleson's character and approach, it seems possible that her personality, combined with the heavy workload, did not help to make Gotherington DNA an attractive place for a district nurse to work. It is significant to note that, after Elizabeth died in 1916 and Mrs Ratcliff of Southam assumed responsibility for the DNA, Nurse Scott remained in her post from 1917 until 1922, after which two VNMs, Nurse Morehen and Nurse Slade, shared the work between them, both still being in their posts in 1925.[22]

By comparison, the Badminton DNA, run by the Duchess of Beaufort, employed only four nurses between 1905 and 1925. Margaret Williams, who was already in post in 1905, was replaced in 1909 by Nurse Corns, who remained until 1912. Alexina Cowee, who had worked at Minchinhampton from 1909 to 1913, transferred to Badminton from 1913 to 1917, and her replacement, Nurse Hedley, was still employed in 1925. Five nurses worked for the Painswick DNA between 1899 and 1925: Annie Freeman 1899-1901, Nurse Gibbs 1902-1903, Nurse Dunn 1903-1908, Nurse Hawkins 1908-1912 and Nurse Judd who took up her post in 1913 and was still employed in 1925. Upton St Leonards DNA employed seven nurses between 1902 and 1925, with Helen Moore remaining from 1903 to 1906, Olive Goddard from 1907 to 1911, and temporary nurses until the arrival in

1916 of Nurse Weston, who was still in her post in 1925. Nailsworth DNA fared less well with twelve nurses from 1899 to 1925, though Nurse Dover remained from 1904 to 1908, Adeline Sproat from 1910 to 1914 and Mildred Stephens from 1919 to 1922. However, it was not until 1924 that a satisfactory long-term arrangement was achieved, with the appointment of Lucy Avery, who remained in her post until 1948.[23]

In the county as a whole, the number of DNAs rose steadily from 28 in 1905, when the Gloucestershire CNA was founded, to 117 in 1925, and the constant turnover of staff can be seen in Table 5.2, which uses data recorded by the CNA from 1917:

Table 5.2 District Nurses employed in Gloucestershire, 1917-25

Year	Number of DNAS	Number of nurses	Number appointed	Number resigned	Transferred to other Glos DNAs
1917	74	95	12	10	5
1918	83	112	17	8	2
1919	87	115	16	12	11
1920/21	97	135	22	14	4
1921/22	101	143	24	14	3
1922/23	108	146	10	13	2
1923/24	113	156	17	10	5
1924/25	116	143	23	16	6
1925/26	117	145	17	15	6

Source GRO D4057/1

Senior nurses also felt the strain of their work and responsibility. The County Superintendent, Miss Olphert, resigned in 1906 as the work "was found to be too much for one Superintendent to perform without undue pressure". She was persuaded to remain, with the help of an Assistant Superintendent, Miss Janet Mundy, but both resigned in 1907. Miss Olphert's replacement, Mrs McCormack remained in her post from 1908 to 1917, during which time six different Assistant Superintendents were employed. When Mrs McCormack resigned, the then Assistant Superintendent, Miss Lena Milford, was promoted to replace her. Queen's Nurse Milford had been the first district nurse to serve the CEHQS DNA, arriving there in October 1910. Although the total population of the five villages of Coln St Aldwyn, Eastleach, Hatherop, Quenington and Southrop was only 1,400, the district covered more than 19,000 acres, with "several miles of very bad roads". During her first year in office, Nurse Milford paid 3,243 visits to 127 medical cases and 86 surgical cases, with 27 nights on duty. In addition, she attended 27 maternity cases, 9 of which proved abnormal and required the help of a doctor. Nurse Milford, "who had proved herself such a kind and excellent nurse, ... had worked most willingly and untiringly, ... but it had become evident that the five parishes constitute too large a district for one Nurse to carry on". Milford resigned in August 1912, and was replaced by two VNMs. She temporarily left district nursing and became Matron of Fairford Cottage Hospital until her appointment as Assistant County Superintendent in July 1916. After only seven months, she was promoted to County Superintendent and remained in office until 1946. Each year, the Gloucestershire CNA acknowledged its appreciation of Milford's devotion and stabilising influence, a typical comment from the Annual Report of 1921/22 being:

> The Committee feel that they cannot speak too highly of the work of their Superintendent, Miss Milford; her zeal and enthusiasm seem to increase with the work, which becomes more arduous as time goes on and as the number of Associations increases. Her sound judgment and impartial justice are always to be depended on, by both Secretaries and Nurses, who one and all pay many tributes to her tactful and sympathetic help in all their difficulties.[24]

Where reasons are recorded in surviving records, the most frequent cause of resignation was ill health: Fanny Mellor at Gotherington in 1904; at Nailsworth, Nurse Overshott (1902), Nurse Dover (1908) and Adeline Sproat (1914); at Upton St Leonards, Helen Moore in 1907 and Olive Goddard in 1911. At the CEHQS DNA, Lena Milford's replacement for Eastleach and Southrop, Nurse Poulton, suffered a complete breakdown in health after less than three months in her post in 1912, and in January 1913 she was reported to have "been many weeks in hospital, with little hope of ever resuming her vocation as nurse". Nurse Coventry, who took up her post at Coln St Aldwyn, Hatherop and Quenington in May 1913, had "a bad attack of rheumatism in July, which entailed giving her leave for a month. ... Unluckily, as winter approached, she was again troubled with rheumatism, and in consequence gave up her place on December 20th." In 1916, the CEHQS Committee were obliged to release Nurse Lawrence from her contract after a year in her post at Eastleach and Southrop as "unfortunately the bicycling during the autumn gales overtaxed her strength, and she was forbidden by her doctor to do any work after the 19th October till February". In both 1918 and 1919, one nurse in the county had to be released from her contract, "her health having broken down", and another in 1918 "was obliged to take three months' rest during training". In 1921, Miss Milford reported to the CNA Committee that "Nurse Fitzgerald, nurse at Wickwar, had broken down in health. The doctor ordered three months rest", and in February 1924 it was reported that "5 nurses had been off duty ill for periods from 6 to 10 weeks, but have returned to duty. 5 nurses still off duty ill."[25]

As a deterrent to VNMs failing to complete their three years post-training agreement, the Gloucestershire CNA Committee decided in 1912 "to raise the penalty for nurses breaking their contracts with the Association from £10 in the first year to £20, in the second year £15 and in the third £10". In view of the salaries paid to VNMs (see Chapter Six), these penalties were severe, but several nurses still broke their contracts. In 1916, Nurse Amer resigned during her first year at Hucclecote, and in 1918 it was reported that Nurse Bailey "had disappeared at the end of 1 years training after refusing to carry out her contract". When Nurse Smith resigned to be married during her third year at Dumbleton in 1921, it was recorded that

> She was by her agreement with the County liable to pay £10 but would find it difficult to do so. She had been reminded, before she married, of this liability and also had not told her husband. After some discussion, it was ... agreed that she should pay £5 instead of £10 and that she might if more convenient pay it by £1 instalments in five months.[26]

Such resignations were clearly a national problem, as in April 1922, QVJI sent a letter to all CNAs "asking for particulars of nurses who had broken their contracts during the last 3 years". It was felt that the terms of the contract should be strictly enforced, so when Nurse Hussell broke her agreement during her second year at Chedworth in the same month that QVJI issued its circular, the Gloucestershire CNA "decided that she must pay the full penalty. ... She had not been very satisfactory and had fully understood the conditions when she trained." When Nurse Hussell "made no attempt to pay the penalty", it was decided "to send her a lawyer's letter", to which no reply was received, and the CNA was then advised that "it was a case which could be pursued". However, "after some discussion, it was decided that in view of possible hardship to the children, the case should not be taken up and that Mrs Hussell should be told that the Committee had only come to this decision on account of her children".[27]

No such sympathy was shown to Nurse Blake when she broke her contract in 1925 and failed to reply to two letters asking her to pay the penalty of £20. It was decided to pursue the matter as a test case and solicitors were instructed to prosecute the former nurse. A date was set for the trial, but the case was settled out of court, "the husband undertaking to pay £2 a month".[28]

A dislike of rural work drove other district nurses to resign: at Hardwicke in 1896/7, it was recorded that "Nurse Phillips ... having so much anxious work ... is leaving us in the Spring ... to take up work in her own home of Newport". Janet Mundy, the first Assistant County Superintendent, resigned after only three months in her post in 1907, "as Gloucestershire did not suit her". At Gotherington, Kate Hastings left in 1909 "to take up duty as one of a group of nurses in a large borough"; in 1911 Bessie Taylor was offered "a position near London ... which she much preferred to country work"; and in 1914 Mildred Griffiths was "invited by the County Medical Officer of Health to take up a branch of special work in Gloucester". At Nailsworth, Nurse Fulton "accepted another post in Cardiff" in 1900; Nurse Warren left in 1904 "to take up a post in London"; Lily Tatton left in 1915 "to accept a very good appointment in Cheltenham"; and "Miss Mildred Stephens, who had been doing district work for 3¼ years, left Nailsworth on Dec 31st 1922 to take up work elsewhere".[29]

Other nurses preferred different branches of their profession: Leah Garratt's year at Gotherington was her only experience as a district nurse and she returned to hospital work in 1893. Alpha Fenton resigned from Charlton Kings in 1909 "for private nursing". The same reason was given by Nurse Farrar in 1921, much to the regret of the CNA who recorded that "she was a very satisfactory nurse for emergency work and much liked everywhere"; and by the Webb sisters, who left their only post at Cinderford after two years in 1926.[30]

Several nurses, both QNs and VNMs, are recorded as having left to be married: Nurse Carter at Gotherington in 1902; Anna Evans in 1909, after two years at Blaisdon; Nurse Hawkins (Painswick, 1912); Nurse Roberts (Bibury, 1923) and Nurse Allen (Kemble, 1925).[31]

Others resigned due to illness or death in the family: Nurse Gibbs at Painswick in 1903, "on account of the death of her sister"; Miss Palk, the first County Superintendent, who left within a year of her appointment in 1905, "owing to the illness of her mother"; and at Gotherington "Nurse Nixon, who was with us for over a year, had to leave owing to the serious illness of her mother, in June, 1916". At the CEHQS DNA, "Nurse Conry, who took up work in October, 1912, was called away suddenly on January 17th [1913], to the help of a sister dangerously ill, and did not return", whilst in December 1921, Nurse Bridges was granted leave of absence "to look after her mother in Fairford who was very ill", and returned to duty in September 1922. Nurse Jenning left Stone in 1921 "for home duties", and in 1922, Nurse Harris, who had just completed her training as a VNM, was allowed to break her contract as she "had lost her mother and in consequence considered it her duty to live with her father". These latter cases, though relatively few in number, still illustrate how unmarried women were expected to be at the beck and call of their relatives and to place family loyalty and duty before personal ambition and career prospects.[32]

World War 1 also made demands on the nurses' sense of duty. In 1914, the then Assistant County Superintendent, Caroline Lee, resigned her post after two years "to take up work in a Military Hospital"; the Report of 1916 states that "the County Association makes every effort to fill the places of nurses leaving their districts, but fear they must beg for indulgence when delay is unavoidable owing to ... the larger number who are doing war work in various capacities"; and in 1918 the CNA expressed the hope that "future work may be made easier through the cessation of war and consequent demobilization of nurses".[33]

Over the years, there were also cases of nurses being dismissed. At Painswick in November 1901, the Committee acknowledged that Nurse Annie Freeman "has always proved herself an efficient nurse and has been much liked by her patients" but they felt that "having been here two years [she] has become too intimate and inclined to gossip with some of her patients and therefore would do better elsewhere". The nurse was given one month's notice, to the obvious consternation of her patients, as at the following Committee Meeting in January 1902,

> the Chairwoman read a petition, which had been sent to her, signed by many of the Painswick inhabitants, requesting the Committee to reverse their decision and retain the service of Nurse Freeman. It was unanimously agreed that it was impossible to comply with their request and that the Committee's reasons for dismissing Nurse Freeman should not be given.

At Upton St Leonards in February 1903, "the nurse's tactlessness was discussed at length and it was resolved to give her notice to leave in May". At the CEHQS DNA in April 1915, "Canon Wright made a formal complaint of Nurse Coast having fomented quarrels between two Belgian families living in Eastleach, and the President undertook to write a reprimand to Nurse Coast". Four months later, in August 1915, "the Secretary brought complaints of Nurse Coast's conduct before the Meeting and stated that Dr Bloxsome intended ... to bring forward a complaint he had against her also". Matters came to a head in October 1915 when "a letter was read from Dr Bloxsome giving his opinion that it was desirable that Nurse Coast should be dismissed. The Secretary reported that she had been given a month's notice, but had run away a few days later." In 1918, Nurse Dando of the Shurdington DNA "was dismissed by CNA as unsatisfactory", as was one unnamed nurse in 1923/24 and another in 1925/26.[34]

One particularly tragic case concerned the resignation of Margaret Powell at Gotherington in 1908, which Elizabeth Malleson describes:

> In the early part of the year Nurse Powell, called in to a patient living in a very lonely cottage on the hills, found her so unfit to be far from help and even neighbours, that she, with great kindness, made arrangements to bring the poor woman to her own home in Gotherington, to await her approaching confinement. The patient seemed to respond to these better conditions, but when her baby was born in March, she suddenly collapsed in heart failure and died even before the doctor could arrive.

Nurse Powell was so shocked and distressed by this death and "found her midwifery work cost her such strain of nerve" that she immediately resigned. Fortunately, such a caring nurse was not lost to the county as she was offered "a post under Dr Middleton Martin [the County Medical Officer of Health] in his Medical Inspectorship of Schools".[35]

However, by far the most poignant cases must be the nurses who, like Gotherington's Jenny Wolfe, died in the course of their duties. During the influenza epidemic of 1918, two nurses died: "Nurse S. Wright, who was at Mickleton for some years, and was loved and respected by all; Nurse Enos, after only 3 months on her district - she was young, bright, and devoted to her work". Nurse Godfrey died in 1919 after two years at Barnwood, "greatly respected and loved by all "; in September 1921, Nurse Culley, who had just completed her training as a VNM, "met with a terrible bicycle accident" and died in hospital the following day; and in August 1925, Nurse Sutcliffe, who had been at Moreton-in-Marsh for five years, died after a long illness.[36]

As Elizabeth Malleson wrote in 1910, in view of "the life of exposure to weather and fatigue, and the constant calls upon the energy, courage and endurance demanded by the work of nurse and midwife, it is scarcely surprising that only women of exceptional temperament and character should seek employment under such severe conditions."[37]

The district nurses of 1925 still faced many of the practical problems encountered by the earliest recruits in the 1890s. They served extended districts that necessitated arduous travelling in all weathers, often on unmade roads, with no transport other than a pony and cart or, later, a bicycle. Where roads were impassable for vehicles, their only option was to walk. Over the years, their workload increased to include all aspects of Public Health Work, which duties they were expected to fulfil in addition to their routine nursing and midwifery cases. During their off-duty hours, they were regularly occupied with record keeping and were encouraged to update their knowledge and skills through reading and attending lectures.

The strain and responsibility of such a heavy workload were keenly felt by all levels of county staff, from the Superintendent to the VNMs, resulting in a constant turnover of personnel. In the circumstances, it is hardly surprising that the most frequently recorded reason for resignation was ill health, whilst a dislike of rural work drove other nurses to take up different branches of their profession or even to break their contracts.

To what extent the living standards of the district nurses also contributed to their discomfort and discontent will now be considered.

Notes

1. GRO D4057/14 Gotherington album of documents re formation of Rural Nursing Association 1884-94.
2. GRO D4057/1 Gloucestershire County Nursing Association Annual Reports 1905-65.
   GRO D3548 3/1 Nailsworth DNA Annual Reports 1900-48.
3. GRO D4057/14.
   Hope Malleson, *Elizabeth Malleson: A Memoir* (Printed for Private Circulation, 1926), p.161.
4. GRO D4057/15 Gotherington DNA Annual Reports 1890-1916.
5. GRO D4057/1.
   Some Queen's Superintendents, *Handbook for Queen's Nurses* (London: Scientific Press, 1924), pp.22 & 36.
   GRO D4057/14.
   GRO D4057/15.
   GRO D4057/19 *Staverton Parish Magazine*, June 1902.
6. GRO D4057/15.
   GRO D3548 3/1.
7. GRO D4057/15.
8. Ibid.
9. Agnes Hunt, *Reminiscences*, (Shrewsbury: Wilding, 1935), pp.79-80.
10. Margaret Loane, *Outlines of Routine in District Nursing* (London: Scientific Press, 1905), pp.15, 26, 42, 172 & 174.
11. Superintendents, *Handbook*, p.77.
12. Coln St Aldwyn, Eastleach, Hatherop, Quenington & Southrop DNA Minutes Book 1914-46, Hicks-Beach private family papers.
13. Superintendents, *Handbook*, pp.28-9 & 41.
14. GRO D4057/3 Gloucestershire CNA Correspondence 1910-11.
15. GRO D3548 3/1.
    CMAC Records of Queen's Nurses SA/QNI/J.3/11.
    GRO D4057/1.
16. Ibid.
    CEHQS Minutes.
17. GRO P244a MI 13/1 Painswick DNA Minutes 1900-20.
    CEHQS DNA Annual Reports 1911-25, Hicks-Beach private family papers.
    CEHQS Minutes.
    GRO D3548 3/1.
18. GRO D4057/1.
    Interview, 17 January 2003.
    CRL 61G942CHA *Charlton Kings Local History Society Bulletin* 36, Autumn 1996, pp.27-29.

19. GRO P244a MI 13/1.
    CEHQS Reports.
    CMAC SA/QNI/J.3/11.
    GRO D4057/1.
20. Superintendents, *Handbook*, p.76.
    GRO D4057/1.
    Gloucestershire Echo, 1 May 1922, p.5, c. 4 & 5.
21. Superintendents, *Handbook*, p.21.
    GRO D4057/1.
22. GRO D4057/15.
23. GRO D4057/1.
    GRO P244a MI 13/1.
    GRO P347 MI 3/1 Upton St Leonards DNA Minutes 1901-09.
    GRO D3548 3/1.
24. GRO D4057/1.CEHQS Reports.
25. GRO D4057/15.
    GRO D3548 3/1.
    GRO P347 MI 3/1.
    CEHQS Reports.
    GRO D4057/1.
    GRO D2410 Minutes of Glos CNA, 1904-28.
26. Ibid.
    GRO D4057/1.
27. GRO D2410.
28. Ibid.
29. GRO D3549 26/2/10 Papers of Lloyd Baker family, Hardwicke Court, Glos.
    GRO D2410.
    GRO D4057/15.
    GRO D3548 3/1.
30. CMAC SA/QNI/J.3/2.
    GRO D2410.
    CMAC SA/QNI/J.3/30.
31. GRO D4057/15.
    CMAC SA/QNI/J.3/14.
    GRO P244a MI 13/1.
    GRO D2410.
32. GRO P244a MI 13/1.
    GRO D4057/1.
    GRO D4057/15.
    CEHQS Reports.
    CEHQS Minutes.

GRO D2410.
33. GRO D4057/1.
34. GRO P244a MI 13/1.
GRO P347 MI 3/1.
CEHQS Minutes.
GRO D4057/1.
35. GRO D4057/15.
36. GRO D4057/1.
GRO D2410.
37. GRO D4057/15.

Queen's Nurse Jenny Wolfe
at Gotherington c.1895
(Gloucestershire Archives D4057/26)

CHAPTER SIX

THE NURSES: LIVING STANDARDS

Salaries

Baly states that if QVJI "were to attract the right calibre nurses, they had to pay them at least as well as ward sisters in a good hospital and to see that they were housed and cared for properly". Vicinus tells us that, in the 1890s, "a sister's salary started at about £30 and rose to a maximum of £55, with uniforms, laundry, room, and board worth about another £20". In addition, even a newly trained nurse could earn two guineas a week with keep as a private nurse. By comparison, the average annual salary of a female certificated teacher in an elementary school in 1890 was £76, whilst 50% of assistant mistresses in High Schools in 1894 earned an average of £118 a year for an average week's work of 35 hours, plus 13 weeks holiday.[1]

In contrast, QVJI had no standard rate of pay in rural areas because of the diversity of local circumstances and arrangements, with each DNA responsible for raising its own funds. Stocks tells us that, in urban areas, "a typical salary for a Queen's Nurse receiving board, lodging and laundry in a nurses' home would be £30 per annum - a sum which could be achieved by a really high-class domestic servant". This comment is confirmed by a Board of Trade survey in the 1890s which shows that a cook-housekeeper earned an average wage of £35 per annum in the provinces and £41 in London. The application form for RNA nurses states that "the usual salary offered is £52 a year, with uniform"; when it became QVJI's Rural District Branch, the Constitution of 1892 stated that

> the services of a Trained Nurse and Midwife can be obtained at the cost of between £55 and £65 a year. This sum would include a salary of from £25 to £30 to the Nurse; uniform, costing on an average £3 a year; and board, lodging, and washing, the cost of which varies naturally in different places. The cost of a donkey and cart, after the initial expense of purchase, is from 1s. to 1s.6d. a week for the keep of the donkey, and a trifling expense for shoeing and repairs.[2]

In the Gotherington district, the nurse was paid £1 a week from 1891 to 1898, but only 'Part of Rent' was paid at an average of £3 per year, uniform costs averaged £1.15s.0d., whilst 'Feed of Donkey, &c.' averaged £3.12s.0d.

Presumably, the nurse paid the balance of the rent herself, plus food, fuel and laundry costs, which would have left little from her £1 a week. This situation changed in 1900, when expenses for the year show 'Rent, Board, Fuel, &c. - £47.16s.10d.' but the 'Salary of Nurse' was reduced to £30.[3]

Similarly, at Stonehouse DNA, Nurse Taite's salary and uniform for 1896-97 cost £34, with board and lodging costs of £39.2s.2d. At Hardwicke, the nurse's salary and uniform cost £33.2s.8d., with board and lodging at £29.6s.0d. in 1893, rising to £34 and £37.2s.5d. respectively in 1896. By comparison, the Mistress of Hardwicke Parochial School was paid £44 in 1892, with £5 towards lodgings at a local farm in 1889, whilst the upper-housemaid at Hardwicke Court was paid £25, all found, in 1892. At Upton St Leonards, the nurse fared even worse, with a salary, including uniform, of only £20 in 1901, with a further £50 per annum being allocated by the DNA Committee to cover Board & Lodging at £40, Washing at £5 and Bicycle & Sundries at £5. The Balance Sheets for Nailsworth DNA from 1900 to 1902 show £75 per annum total expenditure for the nurse's services, though no breakdown is given. At Painswick in 1902, "the Committee decided to engage Nurse Gibbs permanently: the salary to be £30 a year with 1/- a week for washing, besides Board & Lodging. ... Nurse then asked what extra uniform would be given: this was deferred to the next Meeting." In fact, it was not until the following year, when Nurse Gibbs resigned, that the question of uniform costs was resolved, her replacement, Nurse Dunn, being offered "£30 salary with Board + £5.5s.0d. for Laundry & Uniform".[4]

In rural areas throughout the country, many entire working-class families subsisted on a similar or even lower income: in 1898, the weekly wage of agricultural labourers in the Midlands counties, including Gloucestershire, was only 13s.10d., or £36 per year, compared with the national average of 14s.5d. weekly, £37.10s.0d. annually. However, the salaries offered by DNAs neither reflected the class and education nor the superior training that Florence Nightingale envisaged for Queen's Nurses. The minimum annual income needed to keep even a resident 'maid-of-all-work' at the end of the nineteenth century was £150: as Seebohm Rowntree took 'the keeping or not keeping of domestic servants' as the dividing line between 'the working classes and those of a higher social scale' in 1899, this placed the district nurses far below the middle- and upper-classes from which they were expected to come and affected their social position as well as their living conditions. As Vicinus says, "a middle-class woman who earned less than a pound a week could not maintain her social status, according to her peers".[5]

Hope Malleson attributes the low wages in the Gotherington district to the fact that "it included so few houses of the better-to-do that the collection of funds was always a problem". In every Annual Report, Elizabeth Malleson stresses the need for funds. In 1892, she expressed the opinion that, "in an area where from 2,000 to 3,000 persons live in villages and scattered hamlets, it should not be difficult to collect 1,000 shillings [£50], and these shillings would go a very large way towards defraying the expenses of the nursing work". However, the total fees, thank-offerings and donations from the villages never exceeded £30 per year between 1891 and 1900, whilst donations from Frank and Elizabeth Malleson, their family and friends usually ranged in total from £53 to £73. In 1893, Elizabeth expressed the fear that, "any year these friends may decide that nearer claims will prevent their sending help to our district", and the years 1896 and 1897 both showed a deficit, "chiefly occasioned by the cessation of one large outside subscription, through the death of the generous donor", namely 'Percy Whitehead, Esq', one of Elizabeth's brothers, who had made an annual donation of £10. A bazaar held in July 1898 raised more than £40, which "not only gave for the nurse the much-needed new donkey cart and harness", but also paid off more than half the deficit; the remainder was covered by extra donations from Frank and Elizabeth Malleson.[6]

Other lady administrators were equally generous. When Nurse Mackay was appointed as the first district nurse in Winchcombe in 1904, Mrs Dent-Brocklehurst of Sudeley Castle was so anxious that the experiment should be a success that she personally paid the nurse's first six months' salary of £22 and her board at Almsbury Farm of £13.[7]

So widespread was the general problem concerning finances that in its first Annual Report of 1905 the Gloucestershire CNA included a section entitled 'How to Raise Funds for a Local Association'. In addition to subscriptions, donations, midwifery fees and church collections, the CNA suggested "special efforts such as Entertainments, Fetes, Jumble Sales, &c., to rouse general interest, or to meet special or extra expenditure". At Gotherington, an annual Sale of Flowers was held, which raised an average of £4 per year from 1892 to 1916. The Needlework Guild supported the Cheltenham DNA, making donations of £84 in 1898 and £95 in 1901, whilst at Stroud the local Football Club played a Benefit Match each year from 1896, raising an average of £20. A Needlework Guild was also started in Nailsworth in 1903, its first year's donation to the DNA totalling £6.0s.11d., whilst entertainments raised additional proceeds of up to £25 a year, including dances, concerts and, in 1905, a Pastoral Play. At Minchinhampton, 'Proceeds of Theatricals' amounted to £13.19s.5d. in 1904.[8]

Despite such sterling efforts, Gotherington DNA reported a deficit every year from 1900 to 1902, 1904 to 1907 and 1912 to 1915. Whilst Nailsworth DNA remained in credit, the Balance Sheet of 1905 shows a reduction in subscriptions and donations of £14.14s.0d. and the Annual Report of that year states that, "although the Committee are most grateful to those who have organized entertainments on behalf of the Association, they feel that a steady income derived from subscriptions is a far better basis for satisfactory results".[9]

In addition to raising sufficient funds to cover the nurses' salaries and living costs, medicines and dressings also had to be purchased, with Gotherington DNA spending an average of £4.7s.6d. per year between 1900 and 1909, whilst Nailsworth DNA spent an average of £5.9s.0d. annually between 1900 and 1907. Wear and tear caused by unmade country roads necessitated regular expenditure on the nurses' bicycles. At Stonehouse DNA, £2.6s.6d. was recorded as 'Repairs to bicycle' in 1896-7; at Gotherington an average of £2 per year was spent on repairs or replacements between 1902 and 1916; and Nailsworth DNA bought a new bicycle in 1909 at a cost of £8.1s.3d. From 1905, an Affiliation Fee of 10s.0d. per year had to be paid to the CNA, together with fees for temporary and holiday nurses. When Nurse Dover was taken ill at Nailsworth in 1906, the cost of supply nurses amounted to £11.15s.5d., whilst Gotherington DNA spent an average of £4.6s.0d. per year on 'Holiday Nurse' and 'Extra Nurse' between 1909 and 1915. Day to day administrative costs, including stationery and postage, amounted to an average of £2.16s.0d. per year both at Gotherington and Nailsworth, and from 1907 DNAs were encouraged to "insure their Nurses through the agency of the Queen's Institute against sickness" at a rate of 3d. per week, 13s.0d. per year, for each nurse.[10]

By 1909, according to a booklet issued by QVJI, the annual estimated cost of employing a Queen's Nurse had risen to £85-100, whilst a county-trained VNM could be maintained for a maximum of £50 a year. The former average salary of £30 a year was now the required minimum for a Queen's Nurse, "independent of local conditions", rising to £32 and £35 in the second and third years of service, with an additional £2 a year for practising midwifery and an annual allowance of £4 for uniform. Board and lodging, and laundry, or equivalent allowances, also had to be provided. Nationally, VNMs were paid "from 14s. a week, rising to 16s., 18s., or £1 a week", i.e. £25-50 a year, which covered salary, board, lodging and laundry, with uniform provided. In Gloucestershire, it was decided in 1906 to pay VNMs "a salary of £35 to £40 inclusive during the three years they work for the Association" plus uniform. By 1908, the VNMs were clearly beginning to realise their value in remote rural districts, as it was noted by the CNA that, "owing to the increased demand for Village Nurses they now ask larger salaries" and it was decided to increase their pay to £50-52 per year inclusive. However, despite this rise, when increases in the cost of living are taken into account, the nurses' standard of living must have been lower in 1909 than the original Nurse Mary at Gotherington, who was paid £1 a week in 1885.[11]

Unfortunately, the Gotherington Annual Reports show the combined total for 'Salary, Rent & Board of Nurse' from 1909 to 1916, instead of separate figures, so a detailed breakdown cannot be compared with earlier years. However, the average total cost amounted to £88.15s.0d. per year during that period, compared with £78 in 1900. At Upton St Leonards, Queen's Nurse Olive Goddard was appointed in 1907 at the minimum salary of £30, plus uniform allowance of £4, with requisite and sundry costs of £50 unchanged from 1901. When Nurse Hawkins was interviewed at Painswick DNA in 1908, with three years' experience as a district nurse, she stated "that she would prefer sums for Board, Laundry etc. should be included in her salary and paid direct to her; and agreed to the salary of £75 inclusive". Nailsworth DNA paid Queen's Nurse Adeline Sproat an all inclusive salary of £90 in 1911, rising to £95 in 1912; it remained at this figure until 1914, after which the accounts were not included in its Annual Reports, "owing to scarcity of paper". At Charlton Kings DNA, Queen's Nurse Ann Newdick was paid a salary of £36 in 1911, with Board & Lodging costing £43.11s.0d., Laundry £5.4s.0d. plus a Uniform Allowance of £5, a total expenditure of £89.15s.0d. The Balance Sheet for that year showed a deficit of £25 and most of the Committee members resigned, complaining that "the subscriptions were inadequate for the support of the Nurse". Fortunately, the deficit was paid off, "largely by the result of a Whist Drive organised by Mrs Fry", wife of the village headmaster, "and a cheque for £11 from an anonymous donor".[12]

Similarly, the Coln St Aldwyn, Eastleach, Hatherop, Quenington & Southrop (CEHQS) DNA recorded a deficit of £6.4s.0d. in 1911, when Queen's Nurse Lena Milford was paid £35 plus a Uniform Allowance of £4, with Board & Laundry at 12s. per week and Attendance at 2s.6d. per week, a total of £76.16s.6d. before the addition of sundry administrative costs. The deficit was made good by a special donation from Sir Thomas Bazley of Hatherop, in addition to his annual subscription of three guineas, and Sales of Work in the villages of Eastleach, Hatherop and Southrop gave the DNA a welcome credit balance of £14.8s.4d. in 1912. In her Annual Report, Lucy St Aldwyn stressed that such expenditure was not excessive, as

> a Queen's Nurse is a person of education and some position in life, who has had an expensive training, mainly at her own cost, and yet her salary is not as much as many village girls can obtain if they rise to be

> cooks or housekeepers in large houses, where board, lodging, washing, fire, and light are provided for them, they have two or three maids under them to do their rough work, and, unlike a District Nurse, they have no call to be out daily in all weathers and at any hour of the day or night.[13]

In 1916, the Gloucestershire CNA warned local DNAs that "the increased cost of living is causing a steady rise in the scale of salaries required". By June 1915, food prices had risen by almost 32% compared with pre-war costs, and by September 1916 they had increased by 68% in towns and 62% in rural areas. By the Spring of 1917, the price of bread had more than doubled since 1914, and by 1918 rationing was introduced throughout the country of meat, tea and butter. Women's war work had led to a general increase in their wages: the starting wage for a bus conductress was £2.5s.0d. per week, compared with the pre-war national average woman's wage of 11s.7d. a week; factory workers in the processing industries were granted a minimum standard weekly wage of £1; whilst women in the shell factories could earn up to £2.2s.4d. a week; and the wages of shorthand typists almost doubled in a year from their pre-war figure of £1 a week. Whilst working in a munitions factory was undeniably unpleasant and dangerous, particularly for those women who worked with TNT, a post as a bus conductress or shorthand typist could hardly be described as physically demanding or socially responsible, yet their wages were at least equal to, and in many cases, higher than the district nurses in Gloucestershire. In 1916, the Charlton Kings DNA paid Queen's Nurse Newdick an inclusive salary of £100, whilst Staverton and Shurdington DNAs paid their VNMs £76 and £79 respectively. In the same year, the CEHQS DNA, which then employed two VNMs instead of one Queen's Nurse, raised their salaries from £52 to £60 inclusive, and at Painswick, VNM Nurse Judd's salary was raised from £70 to £75 in 1915 and was then increased by a further £2.10s.0d. in 1916.[14]

From the Spring of 1916, a Local Government Board grant of £220 per annum was paid to the CNA, to be distributed amongst those DNAs which were co-operating in the scheme of Public Health Work, at a rate of "£3.10s.0d. to each district maintaining one nurse and £7 to each district employing two or more nurses, £10 being retained by the County Association for administrative expenses". From the following year, a further grant of "£14 per annum for each nurse carrying out such duties efficiently" was also paid by the County Council. Such monetary aid was doubtless welcomed by the DNAs, but it barely helped them to keep pace with ever increasing expenditure: in the same year that the first County Council grant was issued, the CNA decided that the minimum salary for

VNMs in Gloucestershire "will now be £60 + uniform". In that month, May 1917, Nurse McKeown took up her post with the CEHQS DNA at a salary of £75 with cottage and uniform, and total expenditure for the financial year ending 31st March 1918 amounted to £139.[15]

Despite these increases, when the QVJI Inspector paid her annual visit to the county's nurses in 1918, she reported that "in some of the districts their salaries appeared rather low", and the CNA responded by setting the "salary of Village Nurses who have concluded their 3 years agreement at £75 a year". However, when a report from the Queen's Institute on the salaries for QNs and VNMs was read at the CNA Committee Meeting in March 1919, "it showed that the salaries of Village Nurses in Gloucestershire were [still] lower than those in most of the other counties". QVJI's suggested scale of salaries for VNMs was:

> With population under 1000 - £89 rising to £99 by annual increments of £2.10s.0d.
> For population between 1000 to 2000 - £94 rising in the same way to £109.
> For population between 2000 to 3000 - £106.16s.0d. rising to £121.16s.0d.

At the CEHQS DNA, Nurse McKeown's salary for the parishes of Coln St Aldwyn, Hatherop and Quenington, with a joint population of 1028, had been raised in 1918 from £75 to £85 a year which, even with a War Bonus of £10, was less than the £96.10s.0d. suggested after one year's service; whilst Nurse Bridges, who covered Eastleach and Southrop, with a population of 748, was appointed in 1918 at "a salary of £72: this to include her board & lodging at Southrop 17/6 per week and laundry 2/6 per week". This arrangement was calculated "to leave a clear £20 a year for the Nurse herself, the Association paying for uniform and bicycle", but it was £17 (19%) below QVJI's recommended starting figure. Even these wages increased the CEHQS DNA's annual expenditure to £169, leaving a balance of only £14.10s.0d. in hand. At Painswick, which had a population of 2828, Nurse Judd's salary had been increased in January 1919 to £82.12s.0d. per annum, £39.4s.0d. (32%) less than the £121.16s.0d. suggested by QVJI after six years of service.[16]

By 1919, the nurses' living standards had become such "a source of acute anxiety to the Public Authorities [that] a special Sub-Committee, consisting of members of the Health & Housing Committee and representatives of the Gloucestershire County Nursing Association was appointed to consider the matter and to report thereon to the County Council". As a result of their findings, it was decided to recommend an all inclusive salary of £140 per annum for Queen's Nurses whilst the suggested scale of salaries for VNMs was:

1st year after training - a minimum salary of £26 plus £65 for board & lodging.
2nd year - a minimum salary of £32 plus £65 for board & lodging.
3rd year - a minimum salary of £40 plus £65 for board & lodging.
4th & subsequent years £120 inclusive.

This offered a range of £91-120 inclusive, based on experience, compared with the £89-121.16s.0d., based on the population of the district, as suggested by QVJI.[17]

The following financial year, 1920/21, it was reported by the CNA that salaries "have been substantially raised in almost every district", but to achieve this "Associations are in most cases charging higher fees, and asking a regular subscription for General Nursing of not less than one penny a week", with a minimum Midwifery Fee of 15s.0d. Unfortunately, few DNA records survive for the years 1920-25, but handwritten notes on the official copy of the CNA's Annual Report of 1919 show a figure of £120 beside the names of 43 VNMs. Fifteen others are noted with figures ranging from £80 for Nurse Clifford who had worked at Minsterworth since 1914, with a population of only 330 in an area of 1825 acres, to £149 for Nurse Cooper who was appointed at Wotton-under-Edge in 1919, with a population of 3246 in 6916 acres. Of the five QNs employed in rural districts in the county that year, two (Nurse Hedley at Badminton and Mildred Stephens at Nailsworth) are noted at £140, less than the highest paid VNM, whilst Ann Newdick at Charlton Kings is listed at £150, Nurse Wardle at Quedgeley at £156 and Nurse Williams was appointed for the Lydney district, to be started in February 1920, at £180.[18]

Lucy St Aldwyn stressed that "with the higher cost of living and universal advances in rates of pay, District Nurses are entitled to higher salaries", but the system of raising funds and the sources available remained unchanged, i.e. subscriptions, donations and special efforts. In 1919, the grants from the Ministry of Health (formerly received from the Local Government Board), increased from £3.10s.0d. per nurse to £5, and in 1920/21, grants from the County Council rose from £14 to £20 for each nurse undertaking Public Health Work. These increases were undoubtedly welcome, but, alone, they were insufficient to meet increased expenditure, and DNAs that had struggled for years to meet living costs of up to £100 suddenly found themselves expected to raise up to £140 a year, or more.[19]

At a Committee Meeting of the Painswick DNA in March 1920, the Secretary read a letter from Nurse Judd, one of the county's lowest paid VNMs, "asking for a rise of Salary on account of the continued rise in expenses. Lady Hyett then read a circular from the County Nursing Association urging the importance of salaries being raised. ... It was carried unanimously that Nurse Judd's Salary should be raised to £100 a year." To meet even this increase, it was considered necessary to raise annual subscriptions from 2s. to 3s., whilst non-subscribers would be charged 6d. a visit and "bandages and other dressings should be paid for by the patients".[20]

In December 1920, the Secretary of the Shurdington DNA wrote to the CNA

> stating that unless they could receive special assistance their Committee had decided that the Association must close down and that they must give their Nurse notice in January. They have a very excellent nurse and very much wished to keep her but have absolutely no funds after Christmas [having] ... this year raised the nurse's salary at the request of the CNA.

After careful consideration of the case and a Public Meeting in the village attended by Miss Milford, the CNA awarded a grant of £25 providing a subscription system of 1d. a week was introduced and the DNA made "a very special effort".[21]

Tibberton DNA was not so fortunate when its Secretary wrote to the CNA in 1923, requesting a grant of £20 to cover its overdraft of £14.17s.5d. In response to the CNA's recommendation, the Tibberton committee had raised the salary of Nurse Wright, who had been their VNM since 1915, to £120 inclusive in 1920, with further increases to £132 in 1921 and £140 in 1922. The minimum subscription had been raised from 4s. per annum to 4s.4d. whilst midwifery fees increased from a minimum for subscribers of 5s. and non-subscribers of 12s.6d. to 15s. and £1 respectively. These measures proved inadequate, especially as a new bicycle needed to be bought at a cost of £10.2s.6d. in September 1922, and having reported "very satisfactory" credit balances of £29.2s.6d. in 1918, £24.15s.0d. in 1919 and £19.2s.0d. in 1920, the surplus fell to only £1.12s.6d. in 1921, £1.15s.0d. in 1922 and finally into debit in 1923. At the Annual Public Meeting held in May of that year, the Treasurer, Mr Giles, "stated that it would be impossible to carry on, unless something was done to improve the financial position of the Association," but unfortunately the Committee assumed that a grant from the CNA would be automatic. There was great consternation when Miss Milford replied to their letter by explaining that, whilst all such requests were given equal consideration, the CNA "could not guarantee to make good all deficits". After much discussion, it was decided with great regret that Nurse Wright's salary would have to be reduced from £140 to "£130 per annum, with Cottage and use of bicycle. If at the end of the financial year, a balance of over £5 accrued, it would be at the Committee's discretion to give a bonus." In the meantime, a Fund-raising Sub-committee was formed and as a result of a Whist Drive being held in each of the parishes covered by the DNA (Tibberton, Rudford, Highleaden and Taynton), an entertainment given by Taynton Sunday School children and a gift of £1 made by each member of the Committee, the deficit was cleared. By 1924, Tibberton DNA was again in credit, with a balance in hand of £10.5s.2d., increasing to £13.5s.0d. in 1925, with Nurse Wright receiving a bonus of £3 in both years.[22]

At the CEHQS DNA, the minimum subscription had also been raised, from 2s. to 3s. from 1st January 1920, with midwifery fees of 15s. and £1, to meet an increase in Nurse McKeown's salary from £85 to £95 in September 1919 and to £100 at the end of that year, whilst Nurse Bridges' salary was raised from £72 to £91.16s.0d. in March 1920. Although these figures represent increases of £15 (17.6%) for Nurse McKeown and £19.16s.0d. (27.5%) for Nurse Bridges, they were still below the £105 and £97 wages suggested by the CNA for nurses with three and two years of service respectively. A further increase in Nurse McKeown's salary in September 1920 brought her to the recommended figure of £120, whilst Nurse Bridges was paid £108 in 1921, rising to the required figure of £120 after four years service in 1922. In that year, subscriptions from the five villages served by the DNA totalled £110, compared with £73.15s.0d. in 1911, a rise of 49%, and total receipts had risen from £95 to £250, an increase of 163%. However, in the same period, total expenditure had risen from £101 to £277, an increase of 174%. By 1923, despite CNA grants totalling £30, the accounts showed a deficit of £7.13s.5d., followed by deficits of 13s.5d. in 1924 and £10.6s.0d. in 1925, when Lucy St Aldwyn stressed that "it is very hard to make both ends meet", for even though the lowest subscription asked was "less than three farthings a week", lower than the 1d. per week asked by many DNAs in the county, "a half, or even a quarter, subscription must often be called for several times before it is forthcoming ... [and] there are people who do not subscribe to the Association's funds, and yet, when attended by the Nurse, make no attempt to pay the very small fees asked from non-subscribers."[23]

Whether this was due to a reluctance to subscribe or an inability to pay is discussed elsewhere (see Chapter Seven), but the fact remained that the people most in need of the district nurses' care in poor rural areas were those who could least afford to contribute towards DNA funds. This was acknowledged in the Nailsworth DNA report for 1925, when it was recorded that, "the financial position of the Association is worse than at the end of last year. People sometimes say that the fees charged should be higher but that does not commend itself to the Committee." DNAs were struggling with the same financial problems in 1925 as they had at the end of the nineteenth century, exacerbated by the inter-war economic depression, which affected not only the nurses themselves but also those from whom subscriptions and donations were collected, and this was reflected in the salaries they were able to pay the district nurses.[24]

This was clearly a national problem, as on her Annual Visit in October 1920, after the general increases in Gloucestershire wages, the QVJI Inspector found that "the scale of salaries and allowances compares favourably with that of other Counties". Nationally, it was reported in 1922 that "the minimum salary for village nurses immediately after their training is, as a general rule, £30 with uniform provided", and the Superintendents stated in 1924 that the required minimum salary for a newly trained Queen's Nurse was "£63 a year, rising £3 annually to £75, with all found or allowances for board, lodging, laundry, and uniform" plus an additional £5 per year for practising midwifery. In Gloucestershire, the average cost of Board & Lodging for a nurse was £65 in 1919. When this figure is taken into account, this represents the equivalent of a recommended minimum all inclusive salary for a VNM of £95 and £133-45 for a QN practising midwifery. Thus, these figures verify the national comparability of the Gloucestershire scale of salaries of £91-120 for a VNM and £140 for a QN.[25]

Nurse Judd's £100 all inclusive salary as a VNM at Painswick in 1920 was double Nurse Mary's £1 a week at Gotherington in 1885, and the required minimum for a Queen's Nurse of £63 in 1924 was more than double that of 1909. However, a female school teacher could earn £120 a year in 1918, rising to an average of £200 per annum in 1920 under the post-war national Burnham scale, whilst the recommended wage for a cook-housekeeper in 1919 was £65 a year, with food. Furthermore, by the early twentieth century, the minimum annual income needed to keep that symbol of middle-class respectability, a resident general servant, had risen to £300.[26]

Holcombe insists that Queen's Nurses "had good opportunities of promotion to more responsible and lucrative positions". However, posts as Superintendents of District Nursing Homes were restricted to larger towns, whilst the number of posts available as Assistant or County Superintendents and Inspectors was limited by the nature of the jobs. In 1915, there were 23 county associations affiliated to QVJI and competition for supervisory posts was proportionally keen. Caroline Coaling (Minchinhampton, 1904-9) was amongst the interviewees for the post of

Assistant County Superintendent in 1906, but failed to be selected. She was appointed as Assistant Superintendent at the Victoria Home in Cheltenham in 1909, and the following year she was "chosen out of fifty candidates to be Superintendent of the District Nurses' Home at Southampton".[27]

In 1909, QVJI stated that "the minimum salary of the County Superintendent is £110 a year, rising £5 annually to £120; this covers salary, board, lodging, uniform and laundry". This remained unchanged in 1915, when Superintendents of town homes also received in the region of £110 per annum inclusive, rising to £120, and Inspectors earned £180 with travelling expenses. By comparison, the Headmistress of an elementary school could earn £155 per annum in 1918. Within the nursing profession itself, where Queen's Nurses were considered the equivalent of ward sisters, so the County Superintendents were comparable to Matrons. Indeed, at a Conference of Superintendents in 1922, it was suggested that "it would be better to be known officially as Matron and not Superintendent". Some agreed, whilst others "did not appear to mind what they were called" and one Superintendent pointed out the distinctiveness of the title, saying that "she had always thought 'Superintendent' the hall mark of the 'Queen's'". Estimates of the salaries of Matrons vary depending on the size and location of the hospital. Vicinus states that, in the 1890s, "Matrons earned from £100 to £300 per year with room, board and laundry". Bulley & Whitley, writing in 1894, state that "the matron of a hospital may receive anything from £50 to £100 per annum. In the large London hospitals the latter sum is often exceeded, with the addition of house [and] servant." However, few Matrons could have achieved the maximum salary of £300 cited by Vicinus, as in 1915 it was stated in a survey of women's professions that, "It is only in one or two of the largest hospitals that the salary begins at £200 or rises to £300; a few begin at £130 to £150 and rise to £200, but the great majority of matronships in this country average about £100 a year."[28]

In Gloucestershire, the first County Superintendent, Miss Palk, was paid £100 per annum in 1905. This was raised to £120 on the appointment of Mrs McCormack in 1908 and to £130 a year in 1910. It remained at this figure on Lena Milford's appointment in December 1916, "rising by £5 annually to £150 with a War Bonus of £5 annually", and was increased to £160 per annum in November 1918. However, with the general county increases in district nurses' wages in 1919/20, with recommended inclusive salaries of £140 per annum for QNs and up to £120 for VNMs, Milford's salary clearly did not reflect her seniority and responsibility. From information received from 18 County Associations affiliated to QVJI, the CNA ascertained that Gloucestershire was paying the lowest

Superintendent's salary and it was agreed that "Miss Milford's salary should be raised to £250 per annum rising to £300 in three years - a rise of £15 the first two years, £20 the third year". This represented an increase of 200% since 1905 and gave the Superintendent a salary equivalent to that of the highest paid hospital Matrons.[29]

The succession of Assistant Superintendents, eight between 1906 and 1916 (see Chapter Five), were paid £96 inclusive from 1906 to 1911, when Miss Weale's salary was raised to £102. There was a further increase to £108 per annum in 1913, when Caroline Lee had been in the post for 18 months. With the introduction of Public Health Work, from 1916 six full-time nurses were employed by the County Council to act as Assistants to the Superintendent, each responsible for a specific area of the county in which they co-ordinated the scheme. These included Olive Goddard, who had been the much-loved Queen's Nurse at Upton St Leonards from 1907 to 1911, Margaret Powell (Gotherington, 1904-8), and Mildred Griffiths (Gotherington, 1911-14). As Assistant Superintendents, they were paid £110 per annum in 1916, which was increased in 1919 to £120, rising to £150. This maximum salary was only £10 per year higher than the recommended wage for a QN and half that of the Superintendent, for a responsible, supervisory post, which perhaps helps explain such a constant turnover in personnel.[30]

After salaries, the second problem discussed by the 1919 Sub-Committee was "the absence of any provision of superannuation". In 1907, it had been "suggested that the attention of Nursing Associations should be called to the importance of assisting the Nurses employed by them to provide for themselves old age pensions", but how the nurses were expected to do this, when their wages were so low, was not discussed.[31]

Some provision had been made for cases of serious illness in the form of the 1907 insurance scheme and the Tate Fund, founded by Sir Henry and Lady Amy Tate, from which "grants are given to Nurses who break down in health during the performance of their duties to enable them to take the necessary rest and change". Fanny Mellor (Gotherington, 1903-4) received £5 from the Tate Fund in January 1904, as did Alexina Cowee (Minchinhampton, 1909-13; Badminton, 1913-17) in 1914, whilst Adeline Sproat (Nailsworth, 1910-14) was paid £3 in October 1914. When Helen Moore resigned from Upton St Leonards DNA in 1907, it was recorded that she "would receive £5 from the Tate Fund owing to her illness", and it was decided that her successor, Olive Goddard, would "be insured ... under the Jubilee Scheme", which would provide her with £1 a week in case of sickness. At the CEHQS DNA in 1922, a temporary nurse covering for Nurse Bridges, who had been given leave of absence to look after her mother, met with a bicycle accident and was paid a compensation wage of 35s. a week for two weeks under the insurance scheme. In the same year, Ann Newdick (Charlton Kings, 1909-33) received £10 in sickness insurance payments. However, other nurses, particularly VNMs, had to rely on the kindness and generosity of their local Committee: when Nurse Judd suffered a serious breakdown in health in 1919, the Painswick DNA Committee "agreed that she should at the least have a month's holiday ... and that she should have 5/- a week extra and be given a bonus from the proceeds of the Rummage Sale". There was also a Home of Rest for Queen's Nurses at Bangor, North Wales, where, the Superintendents tell us, "a nurse may stay for convalescence or a holiday at reduced terms", i.e. this, too, had to be paid for from an already limited income.[32]

In 1913, a Queen's Nurses' Benevolent Fund was set up "for the purpose of granting annuities to those of their number who through permanent disablement are no longer able to carry on their work". The minimum subscription was 4s.4d. a year, i.e. 1d. per week, in 1916, by which time nearly £1,250 had been raised. However, "to be eligible for benefit a nurse must have been a subscriber ... for five years and be still subscribing at the date of application". The many nurses whose health broke down within five years would not, therefore, have benefited and, presumably, VNMs were not included in the scheme.[33]

At a Conference of Superintendents in 1922, it was stated that QVJI "had reached a stage when a bigger attempt than the Benevolent Fund would have to be made. Nothing so far had been attempted to help the many pioneer nurses who were now getting to the evening of their life." It was suggested that local DNA Committees, as well as the nurses, should contribute to a national scheme "and the pension given should not be less than £40". It was noted that the Liverpool Committee already had their own scheme "whereby the nurses receive a pension of £20 per annum ... without any contributions from the nurses themselves". However, to qualify, a nurse had to complete fifteen years of service, so the number of nurses benefiting from the scheme must have been minimal. Despite widespread concern and regular discussions on the matter, by 1924 the Superintendents stated that it had still "not yet been found possible to provide pensions for Queen's Nurses".[34]

In Gloucestershire, additional provision was made in 1925 when it was reported that "a scheme, which for a long time has been in the mind of Miss Milford, and one very near to her heart, has now been inaugurated, that of a Benevolent Fund for Nurses, the object being to render assistance to District Nurses in case of long illness". As the title of this scheme suggests that it aimed to benefit all district nurses in the county, as opposed to the national Benevolent Fund which covered only Queen's Nurses, then presumably VNMs were also eligible for membership. Nurses were to contribute 2s.6d. annually and the committee appointed to administer the scheme included "four Nurses elected by the District Nurses of the Affiliated Associations". By including the nurses on the committee, the CNA acknowledged the value of their practical experience of the harsh realities of rural district nursing and, consequently, their ability to empathise, as well as sympathise, with cases applying to the fund. The Gloucestershire CNA committed themselves to "do all in their power to help it" and "hoped that many friends will give to this excellent scheme".[35]

The salary structure of QVJI was based on the assumption that its nurses would all be middle- and upper-class young ladies who, as Lewis expresses it, "considered that a tiny wage rendered the work respectable and genteel by making it more akin to voluntary work".[36] Agnes Hunt had a private annual income from the estate of her late father, as did her friend 'Goody' Goodford, but for an increasing number of such women, work was an economic necessity, not merely a philanthropic choice. Queen's Nurses and working-class VNMs all faced the prospect of struggling to make provision for possible early unemployment on health grounds or for an uncertain old age, when, in either case, they would lose not only their income but also the home that such work provided.

Accommodation

As early as 1876, when she wrote to *The Times* detailing her plans for the Metropolitan Nursing Association, Florence Nightingale stressed the importance of

> providing a real home within reach of their work for the nurses to live in - a home which gives what real family homes are supposed to give:- materially, a bedroom for each, dining and sitting rooms in common, all meals prepared and eaten in the home; morally, direction, support, sympathy in a common work, further training and instruction in it, proper rest and recreation, and a head of the home, who is also and pre-eminently trained and skilled head of the nursing; in short, a home where any good mother, of whatever class, would be willing to let her daughter, however attractive or highly educated, live.

She reiterated her views in a paper of 1893, in which she added that "district nurses ... deteriorate if they have no *esprit de corps*, no common home under wise and loving supervision".[37]

At Stroud, three nurses took up residence at 'The Home' at 4 Castle Villas in 1895, under the superintendence of Miss Blackwell, the district nurse originally employed by Mrs Brynmor Jones' society before its amalgamation with Mrs Playne's scheme. By 1898, their number had increased to six and a new home was rented at 72 Middle Street to accommodate the larger staff. Patients were attended not only in Stroud itself but also in nine surrounding villages, including Amberley, Woodchester and Slad. Similarly, between 15 and 20 nurses shared the Victoria Home in Cheltenham from 1905 to 1925. In 1922, it was reported that "in England and Wales there were 17 Homes with staffs above 10 nurses, 123 with staffs of from 4 to 10, 49 with staffs of 3, [and] 152 Districts with 2 nurses". However, such communal arrangements were only possible in urban areas, and in rural areas the majority of district nurses both lived and worked alone.[38]

In the 1890s, the minimum acceptable accommodation for a rural district nurse comprised of board and lodging in two furnished rooms, with attendance, fuel and light. This was the arrangement made at Upton St Leonards when its first district nurse was appointed in 1902 and a note was made of "2 rooms found at 16/- per week, to include coals in winter". However, such lodgings did not always prove satisfactory or permanent. At Gotherington in 1891, Susan Stanford lived as a boarder with Charles Fowler, a carpenter, and his wife Maudie at the Reading Rooms, but by 1900, Elizabeth Malleson was complaining of "the difficulty of getting suitable and hygienic accommodation for the Nurse". In 1901, Beatrice Priestley was recorded as living in four rooms at Tilke Farm, and Elizabeth "rejoiced that so restful a home has been procured". At Painswick in 1901, Annie Freeman boarded with Alice Seddon, a single woman "living on means" at Sunny Bank, Vicarage Street, but in 1906, "Nurse Dunn asked whether the Committee would approve of her taking a small cottage for herself as she would be obliged to leave her lodgings before long". This was sanctioned by the DNA Committee, but such rented property still did not offer long-term security of tenure, as it was recorded in 1910 that the Chairwoman "asked the Committee if they would be willing to make a grant to Nurse towards the expense of house-moving which she had unexpectedly had to meet, having been inconsiderately turned out of her former house at short notice". It was unanimously agreed that Nurse Hawkins should be allowed "expenses up to £8.0s.0d." Minchinhampton DNA had already provided a house for its nurse in 1904, at a cost of 'Rent & Attendance' at £12.4s.8d., with a further £18.2s.10d. being spent on 'Furniture, etc.' Upton St Leonards DNA had also progressed to providing a rented house by 1907, when it was noted on Olive Goddard's appointment that "it was agreed to furnish the Nurse's home ... and it was understood that the cost of the furniture [would be] about £40".[39]

Whilst the nurses clearly preferred the privacy and independence offered by a furnished house, QVJI, in its booklet dated 1909, insisted that "the nurse should not be allowed to live alone. ... She should be placed where someone is responsible for cooking her meals; otherwise too often no proper food is prepared and the nurse's health suffers." They suggest that "sometimes a mother or other relation can live with her", adding darkly that this could be "a solution of many difficulties". At Upton St Leonards in 1904, after Helen Moore had been in her post for a year, "it was reported that the Nurse would like to live with her sister who would take a cottage". It was agreed that the previous board and lodging allowance of 16s. per week would continue to be paid by the DNA Committee, with Nurse Moore receiving 10s. whilst her sister would be given 6s. At the CEHQS DNA in 1913, Nurse Coventry lived at first at Hatherop "in a large cottage with the F. Smiths' as part-occupiers. The experiment of allowing them the cottage rent free in consideration of their services to the Nurse did not, however, prove satisfactory ... [and] she settled in two rooms in Coln St Aldwyn", whilst Nurse Jenkins lived in a cottage with "her sister to keep house for her".[40]

The problem of finding suitable accommodation in rural areas was so widespread that QVJI issued a circular, undated but filed with Gloucestershire CNA correspondence of 1910-11, in which it was stated that "some of the cottages at present in use are neither suitable nor adequate for the requirements of the Nursing Associations. These should be replaced as soon as circumstances allow, and in the meantime such improvements as are possible should be carried out." Accommodation should be provided for "one permanent nurse, and a relief nurse, for whom a second bedroom is necessary. In addition there should be a sitting-room, kitchen with scullery, and a room either set apart or added, as a district room." Redecoration was to be "undertaken at regular intervals" and "replacement of crockery, linen and equipment" was also the responsibility of the DNA Committee, as were structural repairs. All this, of course, added to the already strained finances of many DNAs, who were urged to "set aside annually" sufficient funds "to meet the outlay on these". At Gotherington, the Balance Sheet for 1902 includes 'Whitewashing & Papering Rooms for Nurse - £2.3s.6d.' and 'Furniture, House Linen, & Crockery - £4.1s.8d.' In 1904, 'Repairs to House & Furniture' cost £1.15s.9d., whilst from 1905 to 1916, 'House Expenses' averaged £1.10s.6d. per year. At the CEHQS DNA, Lucy St Aldwyn and two other members of the Committee personally paid "the cost of cottage furniture for the District Nurse" in 1911. When Queen's Nurse Milford was replaced by two VNMs in 1912, a second cottage was required and expenditure of 'Furniture - £15.1s.10d.' was recorded together with warm thanks to "all the members of the Committee and some other friends ... for articles of furniture supplied for Nurse's cottage". Local help was equally generous at Staverton DNA where, having experienced "some difficulty ... in finding suitable lodgings for the Nurse in this district", in the summer of 1914, "Mrs Welch most generously placed the Lodge at Arle House at the disposal of the Association, after having it papered and painted and put into good order". The nurse paid "a small rent" for the cottage, but this was returned to the DNA fund "as a donation from Mrs Welch", and the Committee expressed its appreciation of this and "the friends who give such practical help". However, at Shurdington DNA in Autumn 1913, when it was decided to furnish a cottage for the nurse, "it was a great disappointment to the Committee that no help of any kind was forthcoming from the district, the whole expense falling on friends in Cheltenham", who covered the costs of 'Furniture for Cottage - £9.15s.0d.'[41]

QVJI produced a detailed inventory of the minimum requisites for a nurse's cottage, which suggests a comfortable, if basic, home. Surviving inventories for Gloucestershire DNAs illustrate how, in reality, local committees struggled to meet even this standard. In particular, QVJI stated that "where electric power is available, full advantage should be taken of the facilities offered", but only 18% of households in the country as a whole had electric services in 1926. In rural areas, the figure must have been much lower, both for electricity and piped water. Winifred Foley, who was born in the Forest of Dean in 1914, recalls: "The wonders of gas and electricity we only knew of secondhand from girls on holiday from service. Candles and paraffin lamps lit us up. ... All our water, apart from the rainwater, caught from the roofs in tubs, came from a well a quarter of a mile away. ... The village had no drains. ... The privy buckets were emptied into holes dug in the garden." These conditions existed throughout Foley's childhood and were representative of much of rural Gloucestershire at that time. In fact, it was not until 1932 that electricity was installed in the nurse's cottage at the CEHQS DNA. QVJI also stated that "in cases where the provision of inside sanitation is impossible an Elsan lavatory should be installed", but the nurse's house at Campden had neither a bathroom nor an indoor lavatory, each of the two bedrooms including a washstand and "chamber", whilst a footbath was stored in the pantry. QVJI's *Minimum Requisites* state that each bedroom should contain a "comfortable, well-sprung, modern bed" with a bedside table and lamp, a dressing-table with mirror, a wardrobe and "some means of heating". At Campden, each bedroom included a chest of drawers, but only one had a dressing-table and neither contained a wardrobe. Both bedsteads were iron, with straw palliasses and wool mattresses and neither had a bedside table. "2 bedroom candlesticks" suggests that there was no electricity and no mention is made of any means of heating the bedrooms, but the sitting-room and kitchen each contained a fender and fire-tools. The sitting-room was particularly sparse, with only one "easy chair", three upright chairs, a table, cupboard and lamp, instead of the "2 easy chairs with covers and cushions", three upright chairs, table, sideboard and "writing table, or bureau, with bookcase" that QVJI specified. Pieces of coconut matting were provided for the sitting-room, kitchen and landing, whilst one bedroom contained "2 pieces of carpet" and the other "1 piece oilcloth" and a rug, though the latter was noted to be "worn out". It is significant to note that an advice book for mistresses, written some twenty years earlier, had recommended that carpets should not be installed "in any room where servants live and move and have their being. ... As a compromise coconut matting or a couple of ... rugs might be put on the floor of the servants' hall."[42]

Coconut mats were also considered adequate for the kitchen and hall of the nurse's home at Upton St Leonards, but a carpet was installed in the sitting-room and one bedroom, the other having a rug. The cottage did possess a bathroom, with a "bath and cover", but no indoor lavatory, each bedroom including "1 china commode" and a washing stand. The bedrooms and sitting-room were more fully and comfortably furnished than at Campden. Both beds had a spring mattress, both bedrooms contained a chest of drawers and "dressing table with glass", but neither contained a wardrobe, chair or bedside table. Both bedrooms had a fender and therefore could be heated, but the provision of "2 oil lamps" again suggests that there was no electricity. The sitting-room was equipped with "1 easy chair" and a sofa, "3 straight back chairs", two small tables and a bookcase. The sitting-room contained a fender and fire-tools, whilst the kitchen was equipped with an oil stove.[43]

Both cottages were adequately supplied with linen, though not as fully as set out in the *Minimum Requisites*, the Campden cottage being particularly short of towels, with only "4 bedroom towels" instead of the 8 hand towels and 5 bath towels specified by QVJI. China and hardware were amply provided, but appear to have consisted of oddments rather than matching sets, part of the inventory at Upton St Leonards reading, "6 teaplates (odd ones), 5 teacups (odd), 6 saucers (odd)". Throughout both inventories, notes such as 'faded', 'worn out', 'odd', 'broken' and 'of no use' are made in every room. As Upton St Leonards DNA only provided a cottage from 1907, the surviving annual inventory of 1908 must have been the first, and the condition of the furniture and fittings could not have been the result of a year's wear and tear. It would, therefore, appear that well-intentioned donations of secondhand and superfluous equipment had been used to furnish the nurse's home, which, like their salaries, hardly reflects the standards of the middle and upper class homes from which Queen's Nurses were expected to come.[44]

Whilst the VNMs were selected from amongst local working class woman and were therefore more accustomed to rural living conditions, the accommodation provided was still often of a questionable and, in some cases, even potentially unhealthy standard. When Nurse McKeown took over at the CEHQS DNA, following Nurse Lawrence's resignation due to ill health, expenditure of 4s. was recorded in May 1917 for "coal to dry out the cottage, which had been empty for several months". An oil cooking-stove was bought in July 1917, at a cost of £1.9s.6d., which suggests that the cottage at Hatherop had previously been fitted with a range, but the new equipment proved "very difficult to manage" and was sold in September 1918. In the same year, it was recorded that "linoleum or cork lino" was to be bought for the "front room" of the nurse's cottage, but it is significant to note that it was to be chosen by a member of the DNA Committee, not by Nurse McKeown herself. QVJI's concern for the health of nurses living alone was recognised, as it was hoped that Nurse McKeown's salary rise in 1918 "would enable her to pay a woman to cook for her when out on duty at night, or extra long hours", but when, in September 1920, the nurse requested "new washing-up cloths", the Committee decided that, as she had just been given a further rise in salary, "she must find these herself". However, at the next Committee meeting in December 1920, "a letter from Nurse McKeown was read asking what was to be done about the wear and tear of articles supplied for her use in the furnished cottage rented by the Association: pointing out that the things were not new when she took them over (more than 3½ years ago) and that she had herself replaced various sorts of brushes". The Committee then decided to pay for what was required, "but the Nurse to make out a list of what she considered necessary, first: the list to be examined by one or two members of the Committee before the purchases are sanctioned".[45]

In 1919, the special Sub-Committee set up to consider the nurses' living standards found that one of the chief causes of the shortage of district nurses in Gloucestershire was still "the difficulty often experienced by Nurses in securing comfortable lodgings or homes" and it urged Committees "to provide houses for the Nurses". However, they could only use what was available which, within a poor rural community, was often only a cottage that the DNA itself had to rent, thereby necessitating the involvement of a third party, the owners, whenever permission was needed to carry out repairs and improvements At the Tibberton DNA, founded in 1912, the nurse lived in a cottage owned by the Tibberton Court Estate to whom a request had to be made in 1918 when a fire grate was required. In 1921, the Title Deeds of the cottage were gifted to the DNA, prior to which "it was decided to ask for the bread oven to be removed also the walnut tree to be cut down before the cottage was handed over by the Trustees". Thereafter, although the Committee no longer had to pay a rent of £10, they became liable for the costs of upkeep. In 1925, concern was expressed about "the flooding round Nurse's cottage" and it was wondered "if something could be done to prevent it. If the ditch in Mr Terry's [neighbouring] ground was cleared out that would help." The painting of the cottage was also discussed and the Chairman "brought forward a small list of repairs which required attention". A total of £17.10s.0d. was spent on repairs and decoration that year, £7.7s.6d. of which was raised from a concert at Tibberton Court.[46]

It was not until 1925 that Nailsworth DNA recorded that "owing to continual difficulties arising in obtaining suitable rooms for the Nurse the Committee, at the request of the Nurse, has agreed to the Nurse having a cottage of her own". However, this clearly placed a strain on the DNA's already limited resources, as it was noted that, whilst "a suitable one in a central position has been secured, ... [it] now has to be furnished". Gifts had already been promised of a carpet, chest of drawers, a pair of blankets, a bath, dressing table and two chairs, a feather pillow and a towel rail, but "a cottage needs numerous things to furnish it [and] the Committee would be very grateful to those who would be kind and help in the work".[47]

The very nature of a rural post dictated that the district nurse should live within the community she served, but to do this, she had to accept accommodation that was far below the standards that Florence Nightingale set out in her letter to *The Times* in 1876. Nightingale believed that the morale, health and reputation of the district nurses would suffer if they did not enjoy the same safe respectability and warm, supportive companionship that her vision of the ideal hospital nurses' home would provide. However, in many hospitals, as Vicinus expresses it,

> descriptions of life in the nurses' home sound like a combination of boot camp and boarding school ... with stringent and often unnecessary regulations enforced by ancient and unrelenting battle-axes. ... Meals were remembered as dreary and hasty affairs, without relaxation of discipline. ... The elaborate system of times off and on made it difficult to keep the dining room clean and the food fresh. ... Little variety and much starch depressed everyone.

In 1887, the probationers at St Thomas' Hospital complained to Florence Nightingale that "the milk has been found to contain 25p.c. of water ... [and] they are very tired of the cold mutton; they would like cold ham ...

and (more) eggs for breakfast", whilst at Queen Charlotte's Hospital in London, it was not until 1895 that the nurses were allowed pudding every day. Agnes Hunt recalls her first attempt to train as a Lady Probationer at the West London Hospital in Hammersmith in 1888:

> The nurses were housed in big dormitories, which they had to scrub out once a week. Their dining-room was in the basement, the food was not appetising and very ill served. ... Breakfast consisted of tea and milk and sugar, all mixed together in a big urn, thick slices of bread and butter, and an egg that had been kept too long. The meal never varied, except, perhaps, in the date of birth of the egg. ... No care at all was taken of our health, and it was no uncommon thing for one or two of us to be warded and seriously ill.

After just three months, Agnes suffered a complete breakdown in health and was forced to abandon her training for a year. Her experience was not unique; in fact, Vicinus points out that the drop-out rate amongst trainees was "seldom less than 30% from the very earliest days through World War One" and she concludes that any sense of the *esprit de corps* that Florence Nightingale strove to develop was only an intensive but "temporary corporate loyalty" based on "homesickness and shared miseries" that left many of the nurses who did complete their training "angry at the waste of some of the keenest women".[48]

By comparison, it is, perhaps, not difficult to imagine that an urban district nurses' home, located within the community that the nurses served, with fewer staff than a hospital, would have created a more homelike, intimate and supportive atmosphere. The Annual Reports of the Stroud DNA regularly acknowledge gifts of flowers, fruit and vegetables that had been "gratefully received at the Nurses' Home", which suggests a cheerful ambience and healthy diet. At the Victoria Home in Cheltenham, thanks were regularly expressed "to Mr Beadnell, who tunes the piano without charge", to "Messrs Webb Bros [who] have very generously supplied the Home with firewood, free of cost" and to "Messrs Jack & Co [who] attend to the hall clock free of charge". The house was supplied with a hot water system for which "the pipes were passed through a large cupboard, and this gives a place for drying the nurses' cloaks in wet weather", whilst "a well-built weather-proof house in the garden" was installed "which could accommodate sixteen bicycles". QVJI Inspectors concluded that "the Home was comfortable, the food was excellent and abundant ... and, though hard work is done, the Staff and the pupils are happy". When Caroline Coaling (Minchinhampton, 1904-9) became Superintendent of the nurses' home in Southampton, she was reported to be "an excellent housekeeper [who] makes her nurses happy and comfortable".[49]

However, many of the rural district nurses who both lived and worked alone found that they had exchanged a restrictive hospital life for one of isolation. In 1906, Elizabeth Malleson expressed concern for "the well-known disadvantage of *loneliness* in rural nursing" and by 1922 the *Queen's Nurses' Magazine* was still noting that "the loneliness of a single district was very trying", but against this must be weighed the advantages of independence and a sense of achievement. Already, in 1915, Morley was writing of a new force at work: "the revolt of the modern woman against parasitism and dependence in all their forms", from the 'parasitism' engendered amongst the middle and upper classes by the cult of domesticity, to the dependence forced on working class women "by the loss of their hold upon land and by the decay of home industries". Even before World War 1, the modern woman was beginning to fight for "freedom to work and to choose her sphere of work, as well as for the right to dispose of what she gains". The post-war economic position of women combined opportunity with anomalies, coloured by prejudice and bitter irony. The loss of so many young men on the battlefields left a generation of women who needed to support themselves. The nation had lost approximately 9% of all men under the age of 55; a further 1.6 million had been left wounded or mutilated. The census of 1911 had shown a ratio of 155 males per 1,000 of the population, between the ages of 20 and 40; in 1921, the ratio had fallen to 141 per 1,000. Consequently, the balance of females over the age of 14 rose from 595 per 1,000 in 1911 to 638 per 1,000 in 1921. In addition, the proportion of widows per thousand of the population rose from 38 to 43. Not only were many more women now unlikely to marry, but also, with inflation, higher taxes and, in some cases, particularly the clerical sector, salary cuts, many professional families were unable to afford to maintain and support daughters at home. In fact, many of the young women who had worked during the war and had realised their own potential, were, in any case, reluctant to resume the role of 'dutiful daughter'. However, many women were expected to give up their war-time jobs in favour of returning ex-servicemen, despite the passage of the 1919 Sex Disqualification (Removal) Act. The Civil Service in particular, despite actually expanding, saw a dramatic fall in the number of women employees from 56% in November 1918 to 42% in July 1919 and 25% by July 1923, at around which level it remained throughout the 1920s. Nevertheless, growing numbers of women, particularly from amongst the middle classes, took up or continued paid employment and the income they earned gave them a sense of self-worth that they had not enjoyed whilst dependent on parental support.[50]

Among the post-war legislation concerning women's emancipation and employment, nursing was finally made a registered profession in December 1919. The newly-formed General Nursing Council (GNC), which consisted of sixteen nursing members and nine lay members, specified three different categories of nurses who should be admitted to the register: existing nurses, who had been practising in a recognised capacity before the Registration Act; nurses who were already in training when the Act was introduced; and those who came into the profession through the new entrance system and who were to achieve qualification through professional examinations. Nurses felt that they had won a great victory in gaining their longed-for register, to which the criteria for admission debarred those who they firmly classed as 'amateurs'. These included VNMs and the Red Cross volunteer VAD nurses who had served both at home and abroad during World War 1, representing almost 40% of the nursing contingent of the British Expeditionary Force to France by August 1918. Nevertheless, despite this general sense of triumph, by the time the first State Registration examinations were held in 1925, there was already a shortage of recruits. The census of 1921 showed that there were 94,000 nurses in England and Wales, an increase of 22% over the pre-war figure of 77,000. However, the number of hospital beds available had increased by more than 140% between 1861 and 1921. The supply of recruits failed to meet the increasing demand, and nurses remained underpaid, overworked and exploited, with probationers working a 59 hour week for which they received an average wage of £20 with board and lodging in their first year, £25 in the second and £30 in the third - less than a cook had been paid all found before the war.[51]

Within the nursing profession, the rural district nurses, both QNs and VNMs, were clearly poorly paid and often inadequately housed, particularly considering the responsible and important nature of their work. However, within their local community, they enjoyed a position of trust and sense of belonging: after Lucy Avery had moved into her cottage at Nailsworth in 1925, the DNA Committee recorded that "it is pleasing to see how thoroughly happy she is and the pride she takes in her home and pocket-handkerchief garden". The potential danger of loneliness was recognised as the greatest disadvantage of a rural post, compared with a shared urban home, but, conversely, it could also offer the district nurse the opportunity to live independently, on her own earnings, outside the confines of the cult of domesticity.[52]

Notes

1. Monica Baly, *A History of the Queen's Nursing Institute* (Beckenham: Croom Helm, 1987), p.42.
   Martha Vicinus, *Independent Women: Work & Community for Single Women 1850-1920* (London: Virago, 1985), p.103.
   Mary Stocks, *A Hundred Years of District Nursing* (London: Allen & Unwin, 1960), p.49.
   Christopher J. Maggs, *The Origins of General Nursing* (Beckenham: Croom Helm, 1983), p.64.
   Miss A. Amy Bulley & Miss Margaret Whitley, *Women's Work* (London: Methuen, 1894), p.11.
2. Stocks, *District Nursing*, p.86.
   Pamela Horn, *The Rise & Fall of the Victorian Servant* (Stroud: Sutton, 1990), p.151.
   GRO D4057/14 Gotherington album of documents re formation of Rural Nursing Association 1884-94.
3. GRO D4057/15 Gotherington DNA Annual Reports 1890-1916.
4. GRO D3548 6/1 Bundle of 9 miscellaneous documents 1896-1928.
   GRO D3549 26/2/10 & 26/2/16 Papers of Lloyd Baker family, Hardwicke Court, Glos.
   GRO P347 MI 3/1 Upton St Leonards DNA Minutes 1901-09.
   GRO D3548 3/1 Nailsworth DNA Annual Reports 1900-48.
   GRO P244a MI 13/1 Painswick DNA Minutes 1900-20.
5. Pamela Horn, *Labouring Life in the Victorian Countryside* (Dublin: Gill & Macmillan, 1976), p.259.
   Horn, *Victorian Servant*, pp.27 & 17.
   Vicinus, *Independent Women*, p.26.
6. Hope Malleson, *Elizabeth Malleson: A Memoir* (Printed for Private Circulation, 1926), p.161.
   GRO D4057/15.
7. CRL 336G 283 *Winchcombe Parish Magazine* January 1900-December 1908.
8. GRO D4057/1 Gloucestershire County Nursing Association Annual Reports 1905-65.
   GRO D4057/15.
   GRO D3548 6/1.
   GRO D2774 3/1 Stroud DNA Annual Reports 1895-1946.
   GRO D3548 3/1.
9. GRO D4057/15.
   GRO D3548 3/1.
10. GRO D4057/15.
    GRO D3548 3/1.

GRO D3548 6/1.
GRO D4057/1.
11. GRO D4057/3 Gloucestershire CNA Correspondence 1910-11.
GRO D2410 Minutes of Glos CNA 1904-28.
12. GRO D4057/15.
GRO P347 MI 3/1.
GRO P244a MI 13/1.
GRO D3548 3/1.
GRO D2465 4/33 Cheltenham DNA Annual Reports 1907-31, including Balance Sheets for Charlton Kings, Staverton & Shurdington DNAs 1911-16.
13. Coln St Aldwyn, Eastleach, Hatherop, Quenington & Southrop DNA Annual Reports 1911-25, Hicks-Beach private family papers.
14. GRO D4057/1.
Arthur Marwick, *Women at War 1914-1918* (Glasgow: Fontana, 1977), pp.137 & 141.
Ruth Adam, *A Woman's Place 1910-1975* (New York: Norton, 1977), pp.46, 48, 49 & 58.
GRO D2465 4/33.
CEHQS DNA Minutes Book 1914-46, Hicks-Beach private family papers.
GRO P244a MI 13/1.
15. GRO D2410.
GRO D4057/1.
CEHQS DNA Minutes.
CEHQS DNA Reports.
16. GRO D4057/1.
GRO D2410.
CEHQS DNA Minutes.
CEHQS DNA Reports.
GRO P244a MI 13/1.
17. GRO D4057/1.
GRO D2410.
18. GRO D4057/1.
19. CEHQS DNA Reports.
GRO D4057/1.
20. GRO P244a MI 13/1.
21. GRO D2410.
22. GRO D4277 12/1 Tibberton DNA Minutes Book 1918-26.
GRO D4277 12/2 Tibberton DNA Account Book 1922-26.
23. CEHQS DNA Minutes.
CEHQS DNA Reports.
24. GRO D3548 3/1.

25. GRO D4057/1.
Unattributed, 'Reports of Queen's Superintendents' Annual Conference' in *Queen's Nurses' Magazine* Vol XIX Part 2 (1922), 25-32.
Some Queen's Superintendents, *Handbook for Queen's Nurses* (London: Scientific Press, 1924), p.20.
GRO D2410.
26. Maggs, *Origins*, p.64.
Pamela Horn, *Women in the 1920s* (Stroud: Sutton, 1995), p.130.
Horn, *Victorian Servant*, pp.30 & 214.
27. Lee Holcombe, *Victorian Ladies at Work* (Newton Abbot: David & Charles, 1973), p.92.
Hughes, Amy, 'District Nursing' in *Women Workers in Seven Professions: A Survey of their Economic Conditions & Prospects*, ed. by Edith J. Morley (London: Routledge, 1915), pp.194-8.
GRO D2410.
CMAC Records of Queen's Nurses SA/QNI/J.3/11.
GRO D2465 4/33.
28. GRO D4057/3.
Hughes, 'District Nursing', p.197.
Maggs, *Origins*, p.64.
QNM Vol XIX Part 2 (1922), 31.
Vicinus, *Independent Women*, p.103.
Bulley & Whitley, *Women's Work*, p.29.
Musson, E.M., 'Nursing in General Hospitals' in *Women Workers*, ed. by Morley, pp.181-4.
29. GRO D4057/1.
GRO D2410.
30. Ibid.
CMAC SA/QNI/J.3/12, J.3/13 & J.3/18.
31. GRO D4057/1.
32. GRO D4057/3.
CMAC SA/QNI/J.3/9, J.3/11 & J.3/15.
GRO P347 MI 3/1.
CEHQS DNA Minutes.
GRO P244a MI 13/1.
Superintendents, *Handbook*, p.23.
33. Unattributed, 'Queen's Nurses' Benevolent Fund' in *Queen's Nurses' Magazine* Vol XIII Part 3 (July 1916), 72.
Superintendents, *Handbook*, pp.23-4.
34. *QNM* Vol XIX Part 2 (1922), 30-31.
Superintendents, *Handbook*, p.23.
35. GRO D4057/1.

36. Jane Lewis, *Women in England 1870-1950: Sexual Divisions & Social Change* (Brighton: Wheatsheaf Books, 1984), p.166.
37. Florence Nightingale, letter to *The Times*, 14 April 1876, p.6, c.3 & 4.
    Florence Nightingale, 'Sick-Nursing & Health-Nursing' in *Woman's Mission*, ed. by Baroness Angela Burdett-Coutts (London: Sampson Low, Marston, 1893), pp.184-205.
38. GRO D2774 3/1.
    GRO D4057/1.
    QNM Vol XIX Part 2 (1922), 30.
39. GRO P347 MI 3/1.
    1891 Census.
    GRO D4057/15.
    1901 Census.
    GRO P244a MI 13/1.
    GRO D3548 6/1.
40. GRO D4057/3.
    GRO P347 MI 3/1.
    CEHQS DNA Reports.
41. GRO D4057/3.
    GRO D4057/15.
    CEHQS DNA Reports.
    GRO D2465 4/33.
42. GRO D4057/3.
    Horn, *Women in the 1920s*, pp.65 & 158.
    Winifred Foley, *A Child in the Forest* (London: British Broadcasting Corporation, 1974), pp.15, 17 & 18.
    CEHQS DNA Minutes.
    GRO D6043 1/18 Campden DNA List of furniture & effects in Nurse's House 1903.
    Mrs J.E. Panton, *From Kitchen to Garret* (1888), cited by Horn, *Victorian Servant*, p.112.
43. GRO P347 MI 3/5 Upton St Leonards DNA Inventory of Nurse's Home 1908.
44. GRO D6043 1/18.
    GRO P347 MI 3/5.
45. CEHQS DNA Minutes.
46. GRO D4057/1.
    GRO D4277 12/1.
47. GRO D3548 3/1.
48. Vicinus, *Independent Women*, pp.109-16.
    Martha Vicinus & Bea Nergaard (eds.), *Ever Yours, Florence Nightingale: Selected Letters* (London: Virago, 1989), pp.402 & 403.

Jean Donnison, *Midwives & Medical Men: A History of Inter-Professional Rivalries & Women's Rights* (New York: Schocken Books, 1977), pp.101-2.
Agnes Hunt, *Reminiscences* (Shrewsbuy: Wilding, 1935), p.67.

49. GRO D2774 3/1.
GRO D2465 4/33.
GRO D2465 4/32 Cheltenham DNA Annual Reports 1880-1905.
CMAC SA/QNI/J.3/11.
50. GRO D4057/15.
QNM Vol XIX Part 2 (1922), 28.
Morley (ed.), *Women Workers*, p.xi.
Marwick, *Women at War*, p.162.
Horn, *Women in the 1920s*, pp.53 & 73.
51. Carrie Howse, 'Registration: A Minor Victory?' in *Nursing Times*, Vol 85, No 49 (December 6-12 1989), 32-34.
52. GRO D3548 3/1.
Vicinus, *Independent Women*, p.6.

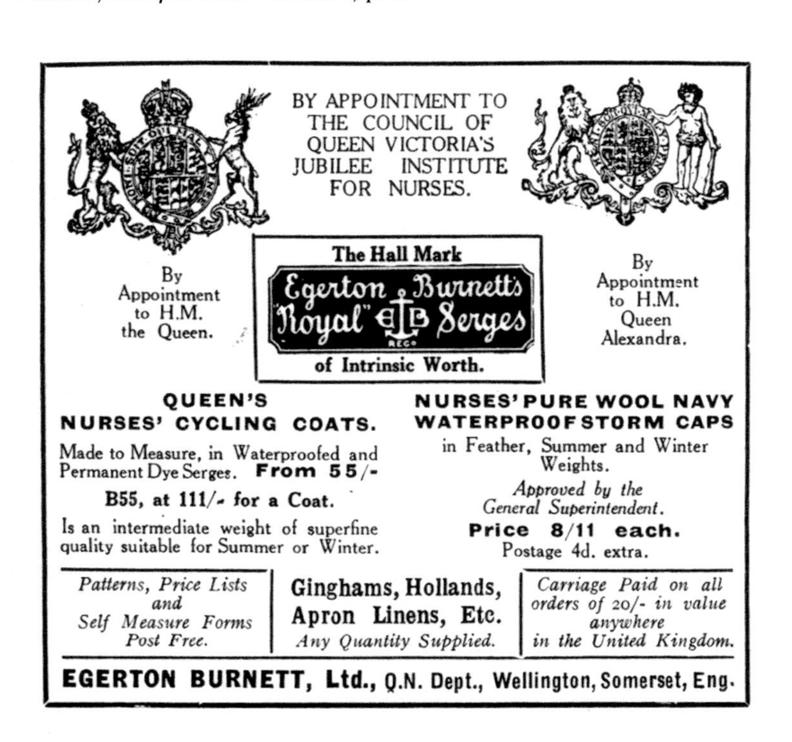

CHAPTER SEVEN

THE PATIENTS

Social Attitudes

The lady administrators and the nurses were clearly motivated by a belief that they knew what the poor needed. However, it is valuable to consider whether the service they provided was, in fact, what the poor actually wanted. Curative care and preventative education were the official dual aims of the district nurses' work amongst the poor, but Fox believes that "it is unlikely that such people had a teacher in mind when they asked for the nurse". Amy Hughes warned that the district nurse's influence might only be transient, lasting as long as she was needed to nurse a particular patient, in which case, "District Nursing becomes merely a means to get people well more quickly than would otherwise be the case, and to keep, if not the house, at least the sick-room a little cleaner and tidier during the nurse's visits".[1]

Elizabeth Malleson admitted that "trained nurses cannot at once dispel the mists of ignorance, or the ingrained bad habits and the prejudice of long custom", and Amy Hughes blamed "the ignorances and prejudices of generations" on "the tyranny of custom exercised by the *grandmother* of the family". She urged the nurses to "speak to the *mother* in simple language as to the feeding and clothing of her children, thus aiding in the national work of raising healthy men and women". Furthermore, the mother could be persuaded to join the Mothers' Union, whilst the father could be encouraged to make provision for sickness and old age by joining a savings club. Sons could be induced to join the Boys' Brigade and daughters helped into service or other suitable work. The Superintendents added that "the nurse should seize every opportunity of making her visit educational, especially where it is the first baby and the mother has everything to learn. Her scope in this direction is almost unlimited."[2]

Echoing Elizabeth Malleson's views of the earliest maternity benefits (see Chapter Three), Loane also emphasised the influence the nurse could exert on first-time mothers, who should be encouraged to take pride in their preparation for the baby: "No nurse should keep or lend maternity bags, nor in any way countenance such an institution. Incalculable harm is done by permitting and encouraging the poor to look on motherhood in the light of an unexpected misfortune." She suggests that the district nurse should firmly decline to accept any maternity case unless:

1. The fee is paid in advance;
2. The mother can prove that she has all necessary bedding and clothing for herself and the infant; and
3. Unless she has engaged a woman to come in regularly to do the housework, wash and dress the other children, cook for the husband, and attend to the mother between the nurse's visits.[3]

However, for the majority of mothers in poor rural communities, the birth of a first or subsequent baby generally *was* unplanned and placed a strain on an already limited income. The taboo nature of any subject remotely connected with reproduction ensured that girls and young women remained ignorant of the most basic facts of life. Winifred Foley, born in the Forest of Dean in 1914, recalls, "Up to the age of eleven to twelve, waist to knees was unmentionable; later than that, it was neck to knees. ... And despite all the evidence Nature provides for the country child, it never occurred to me, or other children that I knew, to connect the two sexes with having babies." Maggy Fryett, born in 1890 in an isolated village in the Cambridgeshire Fens, also remembers, "Didn't know how babies come! I were frightened to death when I had my first period. Didn't know nothing. Didn't know they were connected. ... Our mothers were wrong in not telling us. ... We never knew nothing. And our friends, they were all ignorant too. You couldn't talk to them."[4]

Amongst the letters from working women, edited by Margaret Llewelyn Davies in 1915, only one urban respondent mentions menstruation: "I was not even told what to expect when I was leaving girlhood - I mean the monthly courses." It is also clear from interviews conducted by Elizabeth Roberts, with 160 people born in central and north Lancashire between 1880 and 1914, that whilst, from a practical point of view, it was impossible to completely ignore the subject, in a crowded home with shared bedrooms and no bathroom, most urban mothers confined any discussion to the occasion of a daughter's first period. Even then, no medical explanation was considered necessary and advice was limited to how to use old towelling or sheeting as protection, not to bath or wash their hair whilst menstruating, to keep all such things secret from fathers and brothers, and to keep away from boys. Often even this limited information would be given only to the eldest daughter, who was then expected to tell her younger sisters as each reached puberty. The use and re-use of old cloths, which were then soaked in cold water, could only have added to the physical discomfort, odour and embarrassment experienced by such young girls. Disposable sanitary towels had been patented as early as 1892 and availability increased after World War 1 when factories making bandages and dressings changed production.

However, the cost of such protection would have been prohibitive to any working class family with several female members and, in addition, in rural areas, the distance from a chemist's shop would have made their regular purchase difficult. Consequently, as Roberts concludes, "Mothers undoubtedly gave their daughters a feeling of repugnance about this natural function, as something which was shameful and to be hidden. This developed into a sense of somehow being unclean, and a belief that they were at risk in some unspecified way whenever they were 'unwell'."[5]

This widespread attitude of shame and secrecy also denied young women basic knowledge concerning sex, pregnancy and childbirth. Maggy Fryett married in 1907, at the age of seventeen, and when she went into labour with her first baby, she did not understand what was happening. When she told her mother that she was in pain, the stoical reply was:

> 'That ain't half as bad as you're going to have. ... You're going to have your baby. You know that, don't you?' 'I don't know,' I say. I were that innocent, I were. I say, 'Where the baby come from then? Does it come out from the navel? Have I got to be cut down here?' I thought they were going to have to split me. She say, 'No, it comes from where it went in.'

Three of Roberts' interviewees also believed, as ignorant young women, that a baby was born through the mother's naval, and a total lack of knowledge of childbirth by first-time mothers is repeatedly mentioned by Davies' respondents, one of whom wrote, "When I had to have my first baby, I knew absolutely nothing, not even how they were born. ... I had been in my labour for 36 hours, and did not know what was the matter with me."[6]

The shock and confusion of such an experience can only be imagined, and many young wives, like Maggy Fryett, were left feeling resentful towards their husbands: "They got us like that, and angry we were when they keep coming. You got three and then another one on the way, and another. I had nine. No way of stopping them. If there had been, I would have done." Such a lack of knowledge of family limitation was exacerbated by the fact that any discussion of sex, even between partners, was considered dirty and shameful, and many rural labouring men, like their urban working class counterparts, considered birth control to be unnatural and an infringement of their manhood. Writer Margaret Powell (not to be confused with the Queen's Nurse of the same name) was born in Hove in 1908, the second of seven children. Of her parents generation, she recalled, "Birth control was largely unknown. Mum and dad ...

wouldn't have used it even if they could. In the act of sex the man was dominant. His pleasure came first and he wasn't going to have it minimized by what he thought of as a sort of motor tyre." Of her own marriage, she wrote, "People like us didn't discuss things like that - not working class families. The whole thing was shrouded in gloom and mystery. You went to bed and you drew the blinds and you put the lights out and everything went on in the dark. It was all bound up with the way English people felt then about sex. Even amongst married people it was sort of faintly illegal." Women of Powell's generation, "thought that sex was just their duty to their husbands. They hated it. ... The whole idea of lovemaking was tied up with the idea it was sinful and revolting." Roberts found that sex "was never discussed in the evidence as something which could give mutual happiness. No hint was ever made that women might have enjoyed sex," whilst typical comments written to Davies included, "I submitted as a duty," and "being in a weak condition, I became an easy prey to sexual intercourse". Rural wives shared these views, regarding sex and babies as the price they had to pay for marriage, whilst marriage and babies was the price men paid for sex. Intercourse itself was considered a distasteful act to which women submitted as a duty and endured as part of their husbands' 'rights'.[7]

Even in an urban setting, the use of contraceptive devices was limited by ignorance, prudishness and poverty: if couples were aware of such means, lack of privacy and no running water would have made the use and sterilisation of the cervical cap impractical and difficult; whilst the cost of condoms, at 2s. to 3s. a dozen when a labourer's average wage was no more than £1 a week, was beyond a working class budget and their links with vice, as protection against venereal disease, made them less than respectable. Roberts found it remarkable that in all her urban respondents' evidence, there was a "virtual absence of any reference to mechanical means of contraception". Similarly, few of Davies' respondents mention birth control and those who do all phrase their comments in such vague terms that it is not possible to be certain what methods they used. One mother, who had seven children in ten years, then decided that "artificial means must be employed, which were successful", whilst a mother of four children wrote, "I had to fight with my conscience before using a preventative". Whatever the methods used, the general attitude of urban working class mothers is apparent from one woman's comment that, "I have disgusted some of our Guild members by advocating restrictions."[8]

In isolated rural areas, access to suppliers further made the use of contraceptive devices rare, unless they were improvised. Foley remembers a couple who had only one child: "I once heard a bitterly envious woman saying, 'I 'eard as 'er do tie a rag on a string and shove it up just before 'er do let 'er old mon get near 'er.'" Where any form of birth control was practised by the rural poor, the two most common methods appear to have been coitus interruptus and abstinence, the latter not always with the husband's agreement: Aida Hayhoe, born in 1892 and married to a village blacksmith, recalls, "I'd sit up at night, after my husband had gone to bed, mending the clothes. ... See, I had three children. And I didn't want no more. My mother had fourteen children and I didn't want that. So if I stayed up mending, my husband would be asleep when I come to bed." Coitus interruptus suggests at least an element of co-operation between husband and wife, but was still regarded as selfish, as Flora Thompson recalls:

> One obvious method of birth control, culled from the Old Testament, was known in the hamlet and practised by one couple, which had managed to keep their family down to four. The wife told their secret to another woman, thinking to help her; but it only brought scorn down on her own head. ... But, although they protested so volubly ... they must have sometimes rebelled in secret, for there was great bitterness in the tone in which in another mood they would say: 'The wife ought to have the first child and the husband the second, then there wouldn't ever be any more.'[9]

To such women, the views and attitudes of philanthropists like Elizabeth Malleson and nurses such as Margaret Loane must have seemed patronising and tactless by emphasising happy thriftfulness, pride and forethought as the essential elements of expectant motherhood. As Flora Thompson's mother said to her in later life, poor rural women would have preferred

> 'if they made it a bit easier for people, dividing it out a bit, so to speak, by taking over some of the money worry. It's never seemed fair to my mind that the one who's got to go through all a confinement means should have to scrape and pinch beforehand to save a bit as well. Then there's the other child or children. What mother wants to rob those she's already got by bringing in another to share what there's too little of already?'

Foley, whose elder brother and sister both died in infancy, vividly remembers the "one constant nagging irritation: hunger. We knew that the wages our dads brought home from the pit were not enough to keep us out of debt, leave alone fill our bellies properly. We tried not to make matters worse by worrying our mothers for food." Margaret Powell's mother "often used to say to me, 'If only I could be sure of two pounds a week I'd be in heaven.'" Over the years, "more babies arrived and there was the odd miscarriage. These extra mouths to feed hit mum harder than any of us. She starved herself so that none of us went hungry. Her staple diet was a cube of Oxo in hot water with a lump of dripping added. ... When my sister, Pat, was born, she weighed only four and a half pounds, yet mum had had the full nine months' pregnancy." Lizzie Layton, herself a highly skilled and experienced *bona fide* midwife, sadly recalls how her second son "was delicate from birth and was ill for some months before he died. I was insufficiently nourished during pregnancy and nearly lost my life through want of nourishment."[10]

Mrs Layton was one of a deputation from the Women's Co-operative Guild invited to London to lobby the government to include a Maternity Benefit in the Insurance Act of 1911:

> We were received by Sir Rufus Isaacs, in the place of Lloyd George. I explained the way in which women paid for their confinements. If a woman had a good husband, he gave her all he could from his wages, and the woman had to do the rest, going short herself, as the man had to be kept going for the work's sake, and it would break her heart to starve her children. Sir Rufus Isaacs asked me how much I thought a fair sum would be on which the woman could get through her confinement. I told him that nothing less than £5 would see her through comfortably. He said such an amount was impossible, and suggested 30/-.

However, even after the provision of this first maternity benefit, to which Elizabeth Malleson so strongly objected, successive governments resisted calls for further direct economic assistance, such as family allowances. Concern over the poor physical condition of army recruits during the Boer War had generated the national campaign to improve the health and welfare of the young, but such government intervention was limited by the accepted belief that family responsibilities provided the best and greatest incentives for men to work. The scope of child and maternal welfare was, therefore, confined within the bounds of self-help and education, through policies designed to inculcate a sense of moral responsibility, without increasing the financial burdens of the country's economy by directly relieving the problems of poverty and poor living conditions. As Lewis says, "From the women's point of view help during pregnancy and at parturition was of little use if pregnancies were too frequent, or the mother overtired and undernourished, and advice on rearing children was ineffectual if the mother did not have the means to put it into practise."[11]

Whilst district nurses in urban areas did not act as midwives, other than in emergencies, midwifery played a large part in rural work, as the very creation of the second grade of nurses under the title Village Nurse-Midwives (VNMs) indicates. In their midwifery work, rural district nurses could offer mothers the comfort and support of professional care, but they could not provide advice on birth control or ensure that sufficient food was available for an expectant woman and any other children; neither could they offer pain relief at birth during the period covered by this book. Inadequate nutrition throughout childhood often led to women developing a small pelvis and narrow birth canal; thus poor mothers were likely to suffer severe pain and protracted labour during childbirth, particularly with the first baby. Until the 1930s, only those women who could afford a doctor's fees had access to the two methods of pain relief available, chloroform and 'Twilight Sleep', a combination of scopolamine and morphine, that was more popular in the USA than Britain. It was not until 1928, with the formation of the National Birthday Trust Fund and the appointment of Lucy Baldwin as its first vice-chairman, that a national campaign for the provision of anaesthesia for all women in childbirth was launched. Mrs Baldwin (1869-1945), wife of Sir Stanley Baldwin the Conservative party leader and Prime Minister, and described by Williams as a "rather formidable, ... no-nonsense sort of woman", was herself the mother of six children and was determined to develop a method of pain relief that was suitable for home births and could be administered by midwives without the attendance of a doctor. As a result, more than 1,000 Minnitt gas-and-air machines, which administered concentrations of nitrous oxide and air, were distributed all over the country, but many were not used as the Central Midwives' Board (CMB) stipulated that two trained midwives must be in attendance. As most DNAs were struggling to support even one nurse/midwife, let alone two, "Mrs Baldwin's dream of bringing pain relief to *all* women, regardless of income, was still a distant dream by the end of the Second World War". In 1946, of the 46% of all mothers in England who gave birth at home, only 20% were given any sort of pain relief, and amongst those mothers who were attended by a midwife only, the figure was a mere 8%. Only 20% of practising midwives were qualified to administer gas and air, which was used in a mere 5% of home births. Chloroform remained the most commonly used analgesic, administered in 14% of domestic confinements. Although slow and inadequate progress, it was still an improvement: twenty years earlier, all that the QNs and VNMs could offer to poor women in rural areas, Maggy Fryett recalls, was "a towel to pull on, they used to tie it to the bottom of the bed".[12]

Whilst policy-makers, social investigators and philanthropists paid increasing attention to the problems of poor families and subjected them to closer supervision during the late nineteenth and early twentieth centuries, extolling the concept of motherhood, they failed to provide solutions to the practical difficulties that poor women faced in day-to-day life. Rural wives and mothers, like their working class urban counterparts, continued to endure multiple pregnancies, and births without pain relief, whilst poorly nourished themselves and struggling to adequately feed their families. Doctors withheld contraceptive information on the grounds that it would lead to promiscuity and over-indulgence amongst the poor, whilst clergymen feared that it would undermine the sanctity of marriage, the prime purpose of which was procreation. As a result, Richard Titmuss (1958) calculated, the average working class woman marrying in her teens or early twenties during the 1890s could expect to experience ten pregnancies and to spend a cumulative total of fifteen years either pregnant or nursing babies. It was not until 1930 that child welfare clinics were permitted, but not required, to offer advice on birth control, and only to married women on medical grounds. Even then, progress was slow: by 1937, only 95 out of 423 local authorities had explicitly authorised their clinics to give birth control advice.[13]

At the same time that the importance of women's role as wives and mothers was being emphasised by the setting up of institutions such as Infant Welfare Centres, which Lewis somewhat cynically describes as "combining middle-class philanthropy with the state's desire to save lives by the cheapest method", moral standards were also encouraged and upheld through discrimination against unmarried mothers. Margaret Powell recalls, "It was always the girl's fault if she got into trouble. Nobody ever blamed the man. It was considered natural for a man to pursue and to get everything he could and if he could find a girl that was muggins enough to give it to him - well, she deserved what she got. ... Nothing was done to comfort the girl, or to make her ordeal easy. Her suffering and the suffering of the child was supposed to cleanse her sin." DNAs were never officially banned by the Council of QVJI from offering midwifery services to unmarried women; each DNA could decide whether or not to accept such bookings, though midwives could not refuse emergencies. However, it was noted in 1907 that Cheltenham DNA always insisted on seeing a marriage certificate before accepting a lone mother, and in the same year Gloucestershire CNA sent a letter to all the county DNAs stating that "with regard to the nursing of unmarried mothers ... the Committee considered it desirable in Rural Districts in the case of a first child and that a higher fee could be charged in such cases". How an unmarried mother, without the support of a husband's wage and unable to claim Maternity Benefit, was expected to pay even a standard midwifery fee, let alone a higher one, was not discussed.[14]

During World War 1, a more sympathetic attitude towards unmarried mothers began to emerge, as the number of illegitimate babies, Horn tells us,

> rose from 4.2% of all births in 1914 to 6.3% in 1918. In that year over 41,000 babies were born outside wedlock. Yet, at the same time, the infant mortality rate for illegitimate children was more than double that for legitimate babies. Public opinion was particularly sensitive to the waste of life these figures represented at a time when so many young, fit men were being killed on the battlefield.

This view was reflected in a letter signed by five leading members of the Queen's Council of QVJI, including the Duke of Devonshire as its President and Rosalind Paget as QVJI's representative on the CMB, and distributed to all CNAs in May 1915. It is valuable to quote this letter at some length, as it illustrates the official attitude of QVJI's policy-makers, acknowledging the innocence and helplessness of the children, and urging charity and understanding towards the mothers:

> It has been brought to the notice of the Council of the Queen's Institute that, owing to the rules of some of the affiliated Associations, Midwife-Nurses have been debarred from rendering much needed assistance in cases of single women during and after confinement. The Council desires to place on record its opinion that rules which deprive unmarried women of attendance at the time of childbirth are uncharitable in principle and exceedingly harmful in practice.
>
> How far the principle of punishing the offences of mothers, by neglecting and injuring their unoffending children, can be reconciled with the dictates of humanity and the teachings of Christ, must be left to the conscience of individual Nursing Associations.
>
> The women in question are often open to good influences, especially at such a time, and it appears to the Council most undesirable that they should be deprived of the services and wholesome influence of a good and fully-trained woman, and left to ... the possible risks of hardening and deterioration involved in their being sent to the Workhouse, which is often the only alternative. ...
>
> The well-being of these children, deprived as they are, through no fault of their own, of the normal protection and advantages of parenthood, is a trust imposed on all organisations concerned with the health of the poor and the efficient rearing of the coming generation. The helplessness of this class of children renders the duty of Nursing Associations towards them the more imperative, and there is no

> branch of their work in which a breach of their trust would be more deplorable.
>
> The Council desires to emphasise the special importance of this duty at a time when the War is causing so deplorable a loss of life among possible fathers of the future generation. It would be most regrettable if, at such a time, Nursing Associations could be held responsible for further unnecessary waste of life.
>
> The Council earnestly commends this matter to the sympathetic consideration of the Nursing Associations affiliated to the Institute, and hopes that those Associations in which such restrictive rules are in force, will endeavour to see their way to alter them.[15]

When, the following year, the Victoria Home in Cheltenham wrote to QVJI for further clarification, Amy Hughes, then Superintendent General, stressed that

> these cases should be attended at the first confinement. ... If the home surroundings are fairly good, it is better for the girl to be there amongst her own friends, where she can get into the hands of rescue workers and others skilled in dealing with these cases, and have the proper attention of the Queen's Nurse. ... It is different in cases where there have been several illegitimate children. The mother in that case should go to the workhouse.

The National Council for the Unmarried Mother & Her Child, set up in 1918, also emphasised that first-time unmarried mothers "should be saved from the degradation which too often follows a single lapse from virtue. ... Very many of the men ... have already redeemed their fault by giving their lives for their country ... [and] let it be frankly acknowledged that the women are no more blameworthy than the men."[16]

However, whilst the stigma of moral condemnation towards unmarried mothers was tempered during the war, the dominant social attitude remained one of emphasising the importance of women's role as both wives and mothers in producing the next legitimate generation, improved in quality and safeguarded in quantity, for the good of the nation, as expressed in the 1918 Annual Report of the Cinderford Infant Welfare Centre: "a Nation's strength is the strength of its Manhood. We are working strenuously here with the aim in view to have Fewer dead Babies, Healthier living Babies, Stronger Children, and a Nobler Race." It was, as Lewis says, a state-promoted policy "of healthy motherhood, which did not encompass the right of individual mothers to choose whether they wished to bear children".[17]

Rural Communities

By focusing on mothers in this way, as the key to a healthier nation, the government, and QVJI as one of the main agencies of care and health education, risked undermining two of the most fundamental and sustaining elements of life amongst the poor, especially in isolated rural communities - neighbourliness and intergenerational support. It was what Rose, born in the Buckinghamshire village of Haddenham in 1871, describes as "the village spirit", a sense of unison and a feeling of co-operation that encompassed accepted norms of behaviour and social regulation. Foley recalls that, "When I was a child, the Forest of Dean was remote and self-contained. We were cut off from the world, from the rest of Gloucestershire. ... We were content to be a race apart ... [and] showed a strong solidarity and fraternity." Villagers who indulged in unacceptable social behaviour, such as adultery or excessive wife-beating, were subjected to 'rough music', when an effigy of the offender would be carried through the village, to the accompaniment of banging on pots and pans. Thompson recalls how an adulterous couple were driven out of their village in this way when she was a child and Rose remembers, "Two of these rough musickings happened during my boyhood; and twice I remember how a young man was roped and taken to a pond and there ducked for being unkind to his parents." Even physical punishment was approved by the villagers, if it was considered justified. When two young wives, described by Foley as "a pair of beauties", were discovered to be regularly leaving their children, asleep but unsupervised, to entertain men "in the ferns" whilst their husbands were on night-shift, they were both soundly beaten by their spouses. Hearing their cries, Foley's father, whom she describes as "the kindest-hearted man in the world", merely said, "'I 'ouldn't lift a finger to stop it. ... Serve 'em right.'"[18]

This sense of shared community responsibility also included practical help. Flora Thompson recalls with obvious affection "THE BOX, which appeared almost simultaneously with every new baby ... and the pleasure of seeing it unpacked. It contained half a dozen of everything ... made, kept in repair, and lent for every confinement by the clergyman's daughter." She describes it as "a popular institution. Any farm labourer's wife, whether she attended church or not, was made welcome to the loan of it ... so saving the cost of preparing a layette other than the one set of clothes got ready for the infant's arrival." The importance of such traditions was clearly appreciated by some rural administrators: despite Loane's directive to the contrary, the rules for Amberley DNA, which was originally nursed as part of Stroud DNA but set up its own association in 1912, included, "A maternity bag has been provided for the use of subscribers on payment of 6d a week. Application should be made to Nurse." Foley also recalls that, in the Forest of Dean, "In general the women in our part of the village pooled their baby clothes to help each other out."[19]

Neither would the mothers of Lark Rise have need to engage domestic help, as Loane proposed, for "after a confinement, if the eldest girl was too young and there was no other relative available, the housework, cooking, and washing would be shared among the neighbours, who would be repaid in kind when they themselves were in like case." Margaret Powell also commented on the stoicism and mutual supportiveness of her mother's generation: "The chill of poverty was offset by the warmth of family love." As each unplanned baby was born, mothers "welcomed it and brought it up as best they could. A child just had to take its chance. Life of course was much more of a community thing then. People were in and out of each other's houses, helping with the confinements, doing the washing and looking after the other children while the mother was still in bed, helping with the baby's clothes and requirements." Again, there was recognition of the value of this expression of community spirit amongst some ladies who lived in rural areas, rather than those who dictated rules and procedures from a distance. Whilst she certainly agreed with Elizabeth Malleson of the dangers of neighbours offering unqualified help in times of sickness or birth, Lady Victoria Lambton acknowledged in a paper she read at a Ladies' Conference in Liverpool in 1891, "If we could have trained nurses and certificated midwives in every district we should still need the kind services of the neighbours, for I maintain that no nurse can be expected to do the home work and washing. ... The kind neighbour is invaluable."[20]

Promiscuity was frowned upon amongst the rural poor: Margaret Powell's mother was born 'out of wedlock' in 1880, when "to become an unmarried mother was the most awful fate that could befall a woman". She was brought up in Shoreham, which "at that time was more a village than a town", by her maternal aunt and uncle, whom she called 'mother' and 'father'. "This 'adoption' was not done out of love or even duty by the putative parents but because the disgrace of having a sister with an illegitimate baby was worse than bringing up somebody's else's child." However, villagers showed sympathy and understanding towards illegitimate births if the young couple subsequently married, as Thompson recalls:

> When the attendance register was called out at school the eldest children of several families answered to another surname than that borne by their brothers and sisters and by which they themselves were commonly known. These would be the children of couples who had

> married after the birth of their first child, a common happening at that time and little thought of.[21]

Forty years later, in 1920, Dr Rigden of Cinderford in the Forest of Dean

> enquired the date of marriage of 50 consecutive mothers attending [the Infant Welfare Centre] with a "first baby" and a simple calculation produced the following result: conceived and born after marriage, 28; conceived before marriage but legitimate by birth, 15; illegitimate (the parents subsequently married in one case), 7. We thus reach the rather startling fact that pregnancy preceded marriage in 44% of this series of cases.

These figures, and Thompson's comment, would appear to contradict the predominant views of sex, as discussed earlier, but there is no way of determining whether pre-marital sex took place despite girls' ignorance or because of it. Powell dismisses the belief that "no nice young man would ever suggest such a thing to a girl he hoped to marry" as "drivel because that's one of the things they always suggested. Whether they're likely to marry you or not, they like to try their goods out first." She also points out that, after World War 1, "the ratio of girls to young men was so high that if you had a young man and you cared about him and he suggested this, it seemed to be the only way to keep him. You had a hard job not to do it if you were not going to be stuck without a young man at all." Furthermore, Chamberlain believes that the attitude towards pre-marital intercourse and resulting pregnancy was a result of a "utilitarian approach to marriage. ... In a farming community sons are important and there would be little point in marrying an infertile woman." Maggy Fryett confirms this view, when she recalls, "Well, if you go a-courting, they want that, don't they? He used to say 'What you got under your apron? I got to see if you're any good. I ain't going to buy a piggy-in-a-poke.'" Maggy resisted her young man's none too subtle advances, not because she understood what she was refusing, but because "I were too frightened." Margaret Powell, who began work as a kitchen maid in London in 1923, also recalls,

> The only thing that kept me and those like me from straying off the straight and narrow was ignorance and fear. ... I know that I would never have dared kick over the traces - not because I didn't want to, but because I was too dead scared. I hadn't even the faintest idea just how far I could go without any after-effects, if you know what I mean. So I just had to keep to the straight and narrow because I didn't know where the broad path would lead me.[22]

Lizzie Layton stresses the strong influence of her mother, when she recalls how, as a young girl away from home in domestic service,

> a gentleman ... met me out alone one evening and offered me 10/- to go with him into a house for a short time. I thought of what 10/- would buy and how long I had to work for 10/-. And then I thought of my dear mother. ... I have had many temptations during my life, but my mother's face always seemed to stand between me and temptation.

Foley attempts to justify the belief that the only way to protect a daughter's innocence was to keep her ignorant: "It was no wonder, really, that working-class mothers put the poison in for Nature where their daughters were concerned. After all, they were obliged to send them out into the world at the age of fourteen, with their bodies unprotected except by fear of men and God." Foley does not even consider the option that mothers could, of course, have explained the basic facts of life to their daughters, enabling them to make an informed choice, but their deeply-ingrained prudishness, as discussed earlier, denied such basic health education to young girls and condemned them to a fear of the unknown.[23]

Mothers also endeavoured to instil a sense of chaste responsibility in their daughters by threatening to send them to the Workhouse if they became pregnant, but, Thompson recalls, "at the same time, if one of the girls had got into trouble, as they called it, the mother would almost certainly have had her home and cared for her. There was more than one home in the hamlet where the mother was bringing up a grandchild with her own younger children, the grandchild calling the grandmother 'Mother'." Foley also remembers how, if a village girl in service became pregnant, "she was forgiven. One more younger child had to sleep at the bottom of the bed to make room for her return, and the family food was shared out a little thinner." This attitude was in keeping with the approach recommended by QVJI, whereby first-time unmarried mothers were considered to be in need of rescue and redemption in the home setting, but Thompson herself does believe that rural women's reaction to such girls was contradictory. "If, as sometimes happened, a girl had to be married in haste, she was thought none the worse of on that account. She had secured her man. All was well." On the other hand, to have a daughter home from service who produced an illegitimate child without marrying was considered mortifying for a respectable family. Powell considers

> how strange it was that the slur of illegitimacy was so strong when by examining church registers of the time it was apparent that

> christenings came too hot on the heels of marriages for respectability, particularly in country villages. ... But it was the fact that they did marry the father that made it all right. The great fear was getting pregnant and ... his refusing to marry you.

The sin, therefore, seemingly lay not in the pre-marital act itself, but in its failure to lead to marriage.[24]

Thompson also believes that the rural mothers' assumption, that it was solely a fear of maternal disapproval and the threat of the workhouse that ensured they "'had no trouble with 'em'", was an insult to the mental and spiritual qualities of the daughters: "To those who knew the girls, the pity was that their own mothers should so misjudge their motives for keeping chaste." Foley also recalls that "the standard of morals among the village girls was very high", and Maggy Fryett adds, "Girls got babies in my day. Of course they did. But we thought it was scandalous." Young unmarried girls needed information not fear, education not threats, to enable them to understand their own bodies and prepare them for marriage, unlike Maggy Fryett who, as both an innocent and ignorant bride, found, "That were a shock when I got married. Didn't know nothing. I don't know what I thought I was getting married for." Government programmes for educating mothers in hygiene, self-help and better use of their resources, as implemented by QVJI in both its nursing and midwifery work, did not include encouraging them to teach their daughters the facts of life, any more than it included birth control information for the mothers themselves.[25]

Where that other stalwart of rural community life, the old village handywoman was concerned, Thompson writes in her defence: "She was no superior person coming into the house to strain its resources to the utmost and shame the patient by forced confessions that she did not possess this or that; but a neighbour, poor like herself." Her comment not only illustrates the empathy and understanding prevalent in a mutually supportive poor community, but also highlights the anomalous position of the Queen's Nurses. They were expected to be middle or upper class ladies, brought up in homes where the family were served by the working classes, and they were seen by the poor as superior. In the words of Florence Craven, each nurse "must be content to be a servant to the sick poor" in *their* own homes, yet both the Queen's Nurses and the working class VNMs were seen as emissaries of the rich, particularly in a rural area where the lady administrator of the DNA was often the local 'Lady Bountiful'. They had no official power over their poor patients, yet they represented authority, with all its connotations, not only of philanthropic benevolence, but also of social hierarchy and control. Furthermore, *The Times* could not

> imagine a scheme more calculated to impress the poor, and especially poor women, with the Queen's solicitude for them. ... The entrance of these nurses - "Queen's messengers" they might almost be called - into the homes of the poor, will seem to the latter a direct and individual message of regard from the Lady who is at the head of the nation to the humblest of her subjects, and will help to bridge over the all too wide chasm which divides the rich from the poor.

Lucy Hicks-Beach, the Countess St Aldwyn, recorded in 1904 that, "Reports come to us at the office of the Jubilee Institute of ... the gratitude of the patients ... to the Queen, who they often think has specially sent them [the nurses] to their particular help in their troubles."[26]

However, when Margaret Loane categorised the variety of attitudes most frequently encountered amongst the poor patients and their family and friends, there was no mention of patriotic gratitude. At one extreme, Loane lists those who have

> the kind of faith that their remote ancestors had in sorcerers, spells and incantations. ... With these persons medicine is medicine, and the bottle sent to be shaken and taken for Lotty's slight attack of measles may reasonably be swallowed by grandfather for his rheumatism, by mother for her ulcerated leg, or by Aunt Emma's Tom for epilepsy.

At the other extreme, and "by no means rare among the poor ... are the people who have a physical disgust for all forms of illness, and who allow that disgust to overpower the feelings of common humanity and even to cast aside the bonds of personal affection". She recalls how a strong, healthy woman was "absolutely unable to wash the hands and face of her dying daughter ... because it 'makes her feel that queer'". Such people were only too relieved to delegate all responsibility to the district nurse and to "meet all subsequent requests of the invalid with '*She'll* see to it when she comes!'" Two intermediary groups were "those who are full of zeal and tenderness at first, gradually slacken in their kindly offices and finally become unwilling and positively grudging" and those who were "always full of anxiety to do their best for the patient ... regardless of fatigue, infection and overstrain". By far the most numerous group were "those who are ignorant, but willing and able to learn", and Loane believed that "by spreading a knowledge of nursing, here a little and there a little, local traditions are gradually improved".[27]

The fact that the district nurses did overcome such suspicion and prejudice is a testament to the self-effacing and hardworking majority. In evaluating their success in rural communities, it must be remembered that QVJI was a charity and the poor were not obliged to use its services. The Midwives Act of 1902 forbade the practice of midwifery other than by trained and registered women, but no such Act was passed to prevent village handywomen from attending the sick and dying. In the Forest of Dean, Foley recalls that, after World War 1, "widowed mother Mrs Protheroe" still acted as "layer-out of the dead, to any villager that could spare a shilling or two for such services. She did it for nothing for those she respected if they had nothing to pay with." In rural communities, the influence of the lady administrators in affecting the initial change from handywoman to district nurse may have been difficult for the poor to resist, but once the nurses had established themselves as an integral part of village life, the advantages of professional care quickly became apparent. By 1900, the Council of QVJI could state with confidence that the nurses "had broken down the prejudices which existed in some quarters by their gentle and quiet way of going about their work, and were making people throughout the length and breadth of the land realize that it was the trained nurses of the Queen that they could with most advantage have in their homes." Furthermore, entitlement to the district nurse's care was not means-tested, nor did acceptance of it inflict the humiliation associated with Out-Relief or admittance to the Workhouse. In this respect, QVJI offered a standardised service on terms that included the poorest people without stigmatising them.[28]

Hope Malleson described Gloucestershire folk as "an independent and self-respecting people as a whole", and the reaction of a sturdy farm labourer to being addressed as 'we' in the nannying tone recommended by Craven can only be imagined. However, if the nurse's approach was diplomatic and sympathetic, then Elizabeth Malleson found that "although at first village women have some shrinking from a stranger Nurse ... such feelings disappear before the opinion of a person they like and respect, and there springs up with slight experience, grateful appreciation of better tendance than they have ever before experienced". Having enjoyed such care, one village woman was moved to comment to Elizabeth, "'I suppose God Almighty puts it into the heart of some people to look after others.'" Lady Victoria Lambton of Pembroke also recorded in 1891 that "at first there was much trouble to make the women do as the nurse wished, but ... they have submitted to what they found was really for their good". In the midwifery cases at Pembroke, "the women are unanimous now in praising the nurse", whilst a mother at Kemerton told the Rector's wife, Anne Mercier, "Oh, I cannot describe the difference this time, and at my last confinement; so much comfort and cleanliness. I must always be grateful to the Nurse." A cottager in the same village expressed the feelings of many: "It is just what we have always been wishing for, and never hoped to get", and Flora Thompson, despite all her evocative nostalgia for "other days, other ways", concludes that "the trained district nurses, when they came ... were a great blessing in country districts".[29]

However, over the years, particularly once the system had become established, there were cases of complaints about the nurses' care and abuse of their service. At Painswick DNA in 1912, Mrs Wright complained that Nurse Hawkins had not visited her for more than a week after her confinement and

> the Committee asked Nurse to give an explanation of this apparent neglect. Nurse stated that she had arranged to go for her holiday then. ... Mrs Wright was confined the day before she left and she attended her then and visited her again that evening and asked the doctor to attend during the week. She also offered to call in the Cranham Nurse to attend but Mrs Wright refused to allow this.

The Committee decided that Nurse Hawkins "was not to blame ... [but] should have let the Secretary know what she had done" and it was agreed that "half the fee paid by Mrs Wright should be returned to her as she had only had half the attention due from Nurse". Similarly, Mr Blewitt of Tibberton "complained of neglect of his wife at her recent confinement" in 1921. On investigation by the DNA Committee, it was found that the baby had been due during Nurse Wright's holiday and she had arranged for the Churchdown nurse to attend in her absence. This she had consented to do "and reported the case as quite satisfactory". A letter was duly sent to Mr Blewitt stating that "the Committee considered that Nurse Wright had not failed in her duty" and the nurse herself was assured in writing that the Committee appreciated "to the full Nurse Wright's faithful and unremitting care of all her patients". These cases illustrate how rural mothers not only came to accept but also to expect professional care, especially as Mrs Wright complained that, in the absence of the nurse, she had to rely on "a neighbour who was quite unqualified to attend her", whilst "Mrs Blewitt also complained that Nurse had not visited her since she booked the case, to give her the necessary advice", though Nurse Wright was able to prove that she had, in fact, seen Mrs Blewitt three times and "had been twice to Mrs Blewitt's home and found no one in".[30]

Failure to follow a nurse's advice when it *was* given also led to unjustified complaints. At Quenington in 1915, a complaint was received by the DNA Committee "of Nurse Jenkins having neglected a case of illness, leaving too many days between her visits". Nurse Jenkins explained that "she had been quite unable to do anything for the patient, but had visited her twice, and twice told the relations to send for the Doctor; and when on her way to the house a third time, was told the patient had been removed to the hospital." The following year, another resident of the same village, Mrs Timbrell, complained "of inattention on the part of Nurse Jenkins, when the former had a bad throat. ... Nurse Jenkins' defence was: that she had twice visited this patient and had taken her a gargle, and told her she could do nothing for the throat, but that she (the patient) was to send for her if anything else was required. Also that the patient was under the Doctor's care." It may be that, in these cases, the services of the doctor were not better used due to the increased expense that this would have incurred, but there were occasions when patients simply would not rather than could not pay even the nurse's fees.[31]

The Coln St Aldwyn, Eastleach, Hatherop, Quenington & Southrop (CEHQS) DNA recorded that, at Eastleach in 1914, Mrs Jack Stevens

> still refused either to subscribe or to pay fees for nursing attention to her children on 8 occasions. The Secretary was requested to write to the Secretary of the Nursing Association of the village to which the Stevens family were moving on 12th October, warning her that it was not safe to allow a Nurse to do anything for that family without prepayment. The Secretary was also desired to send a postcard to Mrs Stevens informing her that such a letter was being written.

Two other residents of Eastleach, both non-subscribers, also had outstanding bills for 1914. Mrs Giles received 30 visits from the nurse during that year and it was not until June 1915 that it was recorded that she had paid fees of 5s., after a bill had been sent a second time; whilst Mrs Agg, who had received 35 visits, still owed 5s.10d, despite several requests for payment. When, in 1925, a "report was made of non-payment of subscription or fees owing for some years by Mrs A. Parrott of Southrop, it was agreed that she should be informed that the District Nurse should not be allowed to attend her or her family for the future". Furthermore, some patients were not adverse to blatant dishonesty. In 1923, a fee of 3s.6d was incurred by a sister of Mrs Griffin, with whom she was staying in Eastleach. The fee had been left with Mrs Griffin to hand to the nurse, a fact affirmed by another sister, but by April 1924 it had still not been paid. After pursuing the matter for a further year, "It was agreed that in consideration of the trouble which has fallen on the woman, the Secretary should write and tell her that the Committee would cancel her debt and say no more about it."[32]

Such generosity was also shown by the CEHQS DNA Committee in cases of honest poverty, as in 1916 when the midwifery fee was "remitted in the case of a deserter's wife at Eastleach, who could not receive maternity benefit, nor separation allowance, owing to her husband's desertion"; and in 1920, in the case of Mrs Radway, a non-subscriber of Macaroni Downs Cottages, "she having paid only 2/6 for being nursed in confinement, and there being no probability of her paying any more, as the husband refuses to work, and the children said to be starving". Whilst sympathy and understanding were expressed for the mother's poverty as being no fault of her own, the father was reported to the Society for Prevention of Cruelty to Children. Action was also taken by the Committee of Tibberton DNA in 1920 when "the Nurse stated she could not get the maternity fee from Mrs Williams, Camp Cottage, Highleadon. Her husband had received the maternity benefit but said they needed it for food. The Secretary was requested to write and say that if the fee was not paid by a certain date a summons would be taken out." Three months later, it was noted that a summons had been duly issued, but the result of the case was not recorded.[33]

Mr Williams' defence highlights the main complaint of the poor patients, that the monetary benefits provided took no account of the most fundamental problems of poverty. Clearly, many poor rural women did welcome the services that were offered; in particular, Mary Paget, born in 1912, recalls that in Charlton Kings,

> Mothers thought the Infant Welfare Centre was a very good thing. They could buy orange juice at a reduced rate and buy babies' and children's garments knitted or made by members of the Committee and sold for the cost of materials and wool. This was considered to be a great help by the mothers and a most useful part of the Welfare work. The chance to sit and chat with other mothers was also part of the attraction of the fortnightly meetings, and a cup of tea and a biscuit was an important part of proceedings, but even the 1d cost was not easily come by in some households.

At the Cinderford Infant Welfare Centre (IWC), the mothers also enjoyed a cup of tea and a bun for 1d. and had "some homely talks on Baby's bath, Baby's food and Baby's clothing, Baby Ailments and how to treat them, Infectious diseases, Disinfectants and how to use them ... [and] a very interesting talk on Flies ... [and] the grave danger connected with this pest." Supplies of flannel material and wool for knitting were "sold to the members at cost price, and together with the many patterns of infants' garments provided, have proved a great boon to them".[34]

However, it is also clear that some mothers were happy to take advantage of the practical aspects of the service, but without heeding the advice offered. At Cinderford, it was noted with concern that several mothers were visiting the IWC only to buy juice or clothing, without bringing their babies with them to be weighed and examined. It was decided that, in future, reduced rate purchases would only be available to those mothers who brought their babies to the clinic. Nor was the atmosphere always one of cosy conviviality, as suggested by the Annual Reports which were available to the public. The Minutes Book of Cinderford IWC reveals that, in 1918, one of the mothers was asked "to cease to attend the Club, as the Dr had signified her presence was undesirable, and was keeping other mothers away". Regular attendance at the IWC was encouraged by the presentation of certificates to mothers and by an annual Baby Show with modest, but no doubt welcome, cash prizes of 1s. or 2s., and more certificates, in a variety of categories, including Prettiest Baby and Best Dressed Baby. Whilst such measures may have provided a welcome boost to the pride and self-esteem of rural mothers, struggling to raise growing families, they did nothing to solve the underlying problems of poor housing and low income.[35]

Onc tradition, a habit of generations amongst both the rural and urban poor, that proved particularly difficult for the IWCs to break, was mothers taking their babies to bed with them. There were, of course, practical reasons for this, in an overcrowded home with no heating in the bedrooms, but the district nurses and doctors stressed the danger of the mother rolling over in her sleep and accidentally suffocating the baby. Dr Rigden of Cinderford reported in 1920: "We have always done all in our power at the centre to encourage the use of cradles and show the mothers in case of necessity how to make one for a few pence from a banana crate, but I cannot see any improvement in this respect since we started five years ago." The doctor's records showed that, out of a total of 348 babies under one year old, only 137 (30.9%) had any form of cot or cradle provided for them, the remainder sleeping in bed with the parents. In addition, of 484 babies, 37% had been "considerably below the average weight" on their first attendance at the IWC.[36]

Mary Paget of Charlton Kings acknowledges that advice on bringing up babies was much needed because medical opinion on the subject had completely changed in a relatively short period, in terms of both clothing and feeding. She remembers: "When my brother was born in January 1917, he was dressed as a Victorian baby would have been - cotton shirts tied with tape, flannel binder wound round him and sewn in place every day - terry towelling nappies safety-pinned to the binder - then long cotton and flannel petticoats, long frock." Maggy Fryett adds that babies' eyes were also kept covered until they were three months old, "in case they got too much daylight. You couldn't take them to the window, or put them out. They used to say they can't see till they were three months old, and daylight was bad till they could see. So they keep veils over their eyes. Didn't they have some silly ideas? A wonder they didn't go boss-eyed, ain't it?" All this had changed by the time Mrs Paget's brother began to walk, when "he was put into knitted vests, knitted jerseys and shorts, which were thought to be more sensible and certainly less trouble". Similarly, when Mrs Paget's mother discussed weaning, her idea of bread and milk, as had been given to her older child, was "vetoed in favour of mashed potato and gravy, followed by baked apple and cream (supposed to be easily digested)". However, despite such marked changes in ideas, Mrs Paget maintains that the intergenerational influences, that Amy Hughes sought to dispel, remained an important element of rural life: "There was a lot of poverty in Charlton Kings between the wars and young mothers were grateful for the help they had from grandmothers."[37]

Overall, it would appear that the advantages of trained nursing care and professional midwifery were clearly recognised and accepted with gratitude by the majority of the poor within a few years of QVJI's formation, whilst the success of the educative aspects of its aims remained more implicit and difficult to either quantify or qualify. In this respect, Margaret Loane urged that

> when inclined to be discouraged at the small results of her labours, the nurse must reflect that it is impossible for her to estimate how deep an impression her apparently wasted teaching may be making. ... Information that Mrs G repeats over the paling with a sniff of scorn to Mrs H may be treasured by her hearer as a pearl of wisdom ... or it may be engraved on the memory of some silent little listener destined in due time to be the mother of a dozen children, all healthier and happier for the knowledge that she half-consciously absorbed while her eyes followed the quick movements of that strange person - the district nurse.[38]

The years between the founding of QVJI and the inter-war depression saw great changes within the countryside. There is, of course, the danger of making sweeping generalisations without taking into account regional variations, but the overall national pattern was affected by the crop failures of the 1870s which coincided with an increase of cheap imports of food from the prospering USA and Australia. By the end of the nineteenth century, imports of frozen meat and dairy produce also undermined the position of farmers, whilst the economic importance of rural trades and crafts dwindled in the face of growing industrialisation and foreign competition. The devastating loss of a generation of young men in World War 1 and the change of ownership of some landed estates, exacerbated by increases in death duties, also disturbed the continuity of rural life.

Throughout this upheaval, the rural poor clung to the sustaining elements of their communities - moral codes and sanctions, neighbourliness and intergenerational support. Whilst it is clear from interviews and letters that daughters resented the state of total ignorance in which their mothers raised them, it was still to their mothers that they turned for help and advice in raising their own children. Loane's comment (above) that her little listener was *destined* to be the mother of a dozen children clearly illustrates that the purpose of government programmes of child and maternal welfare, as implemented by QVJI, was to help women raise healthier children, not to have fewer babies. As Powell says, "The whole idea was to have families. ... The more children you had, ... the more you were looked upon as fulfilling your duties as a Christian citizen."[39] A combination of sexual ignorance, multiple pregnancies, poor nutrition, and overcrowded, insanitary housing remained the lot of both rural and urban working class wives and mothers throughout the late nineteenth and early twentieth centuries. In this situation, the nursing and midwifery care offered by QVJI nurses did much to relieve the effects of poverty, whilst social policies failed to solve the underlying causes.

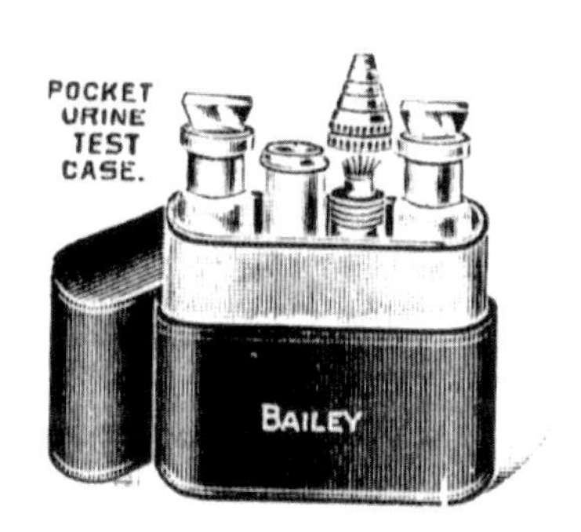

POCKET URINE TEST CASE.

This small compact set has been designed for Midwives practising in rural districts.

Notes

1. Enid Fox, 'Universal Health Care & Self-Help: Paying for District Nursing Before the National Health Service', *Twentieth Century British History*, Vol 7 No 1 (1996), 83-109.
   Amy Hughes, 'Some Responsibilities of Queen's Nurses', *Queen's Nurses' Magazine*, Vol 1 Part 1 (May 1904), 11-13.
2. Lady Victoria Lambton & Mrs Elizabeth Malleson, 'Philanthropic Aspects of Nursing' in *Woman's Mission*, ed. by Baroness Angela Burdett-Coutts (London: Sampson Low, Marston, 1893), pp.206-215.
   Hughes, 'Some Responsibilities'.
   Some Queen's Superintendents, *Handbook for Queen's Nurses* (London: Scientific Press, 1924), p.50.
3. Margaret Loane, *Outlines of Routine in District Nursing* (London: Scientific Press, 1905), pp.107-8.
4. Winifred Foley, *A Child in the Forest* (London: British Broadcasting Corporation, 1974), pp.111-2.
   Mary Chamberlain, *Fenwomen: A Portrait of Women in an English Village* (London: Virago, 1975), p.73.
5. Margaret Llewelyn Davies (ed.), *Maternity: Letters from Working Women collected by The Women's Co-operative Guild* (London: Virago, 1978 edition; first published 1915), pp.187-8.
   Elizabeth Roberts, *A Woman's Place: An Oral History of Working-Class Women 1890-1940* (Oxford: Blackwell, 1984), pp.16-18.
6. Chamberlain, *Fenwomen*, p.73.
   Roberts, *Woman's Place*, pp.16, 17 & 110.
   Davies, *Maternity*, p.50; see also pp.30, 58 & 187.
7. Chamberlain, *Fenwomen*, p.74.
   Margaret Powell, *Below Stairs*, (London: Pan Books, 1970 edition; first published 1968), p.90.
   Margaret Powell, *Climbing the Stairs*, (London: Pan Books, 1969), p.99.
   Margaret Powell, *My Mother and I*, (London: Pan Books, 1974 edition; first published 1972), pp. 5-6 & 110.
   Roberts, *Woman's Place*, p.84.
   Davies, *Maternity*, pp.67 & 99.
8. Barbara Brookes, 'Women & Reproduction 1860-1939' in *Labour & Love: Women's Experience of Home & Family 1850-1940*, ed. by Jane Lewis (Oxford: Blackwell, 1986), pp.158-9.
   Roberts, *Woman's Place*, p.96.
   Davies, *Maternity*, pp.61, 94 & 115; see also pp.73-4 & 89.
9. Foley, *Child*, p.46.
   Chamberlain, *Fenwomen*, p.77.
   Flora Thompson, *Lark Rise to Candleford* (Harmondsworth: Penguin, 1973 edition; first published 1939-43), pp.137-8.

10. Ibid, p.138.
    Foley, *Child*, p.19.
    Powell, *Climbing the Stairs*, p.21.
    Powell, *My Mother and I*, p.113.
    Mrs Layton, 'Memories of Seventy Years' in *Life As We Have Known It by Co-operative Women,* ed. by Margaret Llewelyn Davies (London: Virago, 1977 edition; first published 1931), pp.1-55.
11. Ibid, p.49.
    Jane Lewis, *The Politics of Motherhood: Child & Maternal Welfare in England, 1900-1939* (London: Croom Helm, 1980), p.14.
12. A. Susan Williams, *Ladies of Influence: Women of the Elite in Interwar Britain* (London: Penguin, 2001), pp.45 & 57-8.
    Chamberlain, *Fenwomen,* p.73.
13. Jane Lewis, *Women in England 1870-1950: Sexual Divisions & Social Change* (Brighton: Wheatsheaf Books, 1984), p.23.
    Pamela Horn, *Women in the 1920s* (Stroud: Sutton, 1995), p.119.
14. Lewis, *Politics of Motherhood,* p.61.
    Powell, *Climbing the Stairs,* p.63.
    Powell, *My Mother and I,* p.5.
    GRO D2410 Minutes of Gloucestershire CNA 1904-28.
15. Horn, *Women in the 1920s,* pp.12-13.
    GRO D2465 4/35 Cheltenham DNA Correspondence 1892-1917.
16. Ibid.
    Horn, *Women in the 1920s,* p.13.
17. GRO D2429/4 Cinderford Infant Welfare Centre Minutes Book 1915-30.
    Lewis, *Women in England,* p.33.
18. Walter Rose, *Good Neighbours: Some Recollections of an English Village & its People* (Cambridge University Press, 1942), pp.76-7 & 98.
    Foley, *Child,* pp.13, 15 & 120-1.
    Thompson, *Lark Rise,* p.140.
19. Ibid, pp.133-4
    GRO D3548 6/1 Bundle of 9 miscellaneous documents 1896-1928.
    Foley, *Child,* p.94.
20. Thompson, *Lark Rise*, p.137.
    Powell, *My Mother and I,* pp.110-11 & 113.
    GRO D4057/14 Gotherington album of documents re formation of the RNA 1884-94.
21. Powell, *My Mother and I,* pp.5, 6 & 8.
    Thompson, *Lark Rise,* p.138.
22. GRO D2429/4.
    Powell, *Below Stairs,* pp.63 & 89.
    Chamberlain, *Fenwomen,* pp.71-2.

23. Layton, 'Memories', p.26.
    Foley, *Child,* pp.111-12.
24. Thompson, *Lark Rise,* pp.139-40.
    Foley, *Child,* p.117.
    Powell, *My Mother and I,* pp.33-4.
25. Thompson, *Lark Rise*, pp.139-40.
    Foley, *Child,* p.117.
    Chamberlain, *Fenwomen,* pp.72-3.
26. Thompson, *Lark Rise*, p.136.
    Mrs Dacre Craven, *A Guide to District Nurses & Home Nursing* (London: Macmillan, 1894 edition), p.3.
    The Times, 7 January 1888, p.9, c.1 & 2.
    Gloucestershire Chronicle, 24 September 1904, Hicks-Beach private family papers.
27. Loane, *Outlines of Routine,* pp.8 & 147-50.
28. Foley, *Child,* p.51.
    The Times, 6 July 1900, p.4, c.6.
    Fox, 'Universal Health Care', p.104.
29. Hope Malleson, *Elizabeth Malleson: A Memoir* (Printed for Private Circulation, 1926), p.162.
    Letter from Elizabeth Malleson to *The Nursing Record,* 17 October 1889, p.232.
    GRO D4057/14.
    Thompson, *Lark Rise,* p.136
30. GRO P244a MI 13/1 Painswick DNA Minutes 1900-20.
    GRO D4277 12/1 Tibberton DNA Minutes Book 1918-26.
31. Coln St Aldwyn, Eastleach, Hatherop, Quenington & Southrop DNA Minutes Book 1914-46, Hicks-Beach private family papers.
32. Ibid.
33. Ibid.
    GRO D4277 12/1.
34. Interview, 17 January 2003.
    GRO D2429/4.
35. Ibid.
36. Ibid.
37. CRL 61G942CHA Mary Paget, 'Charlton Kings Infant Welfare Centre 1923-1980', *Charlton Kings Local History Society Bulletin* 36, Autumn 1996, 27-29.
    Chamberlain, *Fenwomen,* p.75.
    Interview, 17 January 2003.
38. Loane, *Outlines of Routine,* p.152.
39. Powell, *Below Stairs,* p.6.

CONCLUSION

When I began my research for this book, I was aware that rural district nursing was a subject that had been neglected by historians, both locally and nationally. This, in itself, presented both problems and opportunities. In particular, secondary sources paid scant attention to district nursing, preferring to concentrate on hospital nursing; thus, only the barest background details could be gleaned from such studies. On the other hand, I found a wealth of primary source material that had not been previously used. Whilst these records proved difficult, and at times laborious, to collate, they offered a unique insight into the interrelated lives of the people they revealed. They also established beyond doubt the importance of Gloucestershire in the history of what grew into a national system of district nursing.

Other historians have identified district nursing as a neglected area of research, and they acknowledge both the reasons for this omission and the questions it leaves unanswered. As Davies says, "Those who have tried to interest themselves in other kinds of nursing will know just how much the sources are biased towards hospital nursing, how they reflect higher social evaluations of this form of nursing and how hard it is to try to redress this." In particular, Maggs points out, "We now understand more fully the process by which the new *hospital* nurses replaced the old but ... we still know very little about those she replaced *outside* of the institutional settings. What, for example, happened to the 'village nurse', and the 'wise woman'?" Where the stalwart of rural voluntarism is concerned, Summers adds that "one can think of few topics more open to caricature and cliche than ... the Lady Bountiful. ... It is one of the tasks of feminist history to rescue women's work from oblivion and ridicule, and to demonstrate the effort, motivation and skills" which such women brought to nineteenth and early twentieth century philanthropic organisations.[1]

In this book, I have attempted to address these issues by using the surviving local and national primary sources to recreate a detailed and authentic picture of the development of rural district nursing in Gloucestershire, in terms of both the significance of the changing role of Lady Bountiful and the lives of the nurses themselves. Consideration has also been given to the reaction of the poor patients to QVJI's official dual aims of curative care and preventative education. In conclusion, it will now be valuable to look again at each of these three tiers of rural society.

It quickly became obvious during my research that Elizabeth Malleson, who her daughter describes as the "potent influence" behind the formation of the Rural Nursing Association (RNA), was not the typical Lady Bountiful that I expected to emerge from the records. When she moved from

Wimbledon to Gloucestershire, her unorthodox, non-sectarian views made her more enemies than friends amongst her new neighbours, but with resolute doggedness, she not only overcame the disapproval of rural traditionalists, she also created new opportunities for the very social group that initially opposed her. Hope tells us that "later in life her character mellowed greatly without losing its strength ... [and a] greater tolerance on religious questions marked her later years ... [though] enthusiasm or indignation would, as of old, stir her to a burst of vehement speech". Despite this later serenity, her obvious intelligence, and her sincere concern for the health and welfare of the rural poor, Elizabeth Malleson remains a character who demands respect, but is difficult to *like,* particularly when compared with her close co-worker, the altruistic and compassionate Lucy Hicks-Beach, Countess St Aldwyn. Nevertheless, Elizabeth's influence on the development of rural district nursing, both locally and nationally, is undoubted. By 1892, her reputation was such that she was called before the Select Committee of the House of Commons considering The Registration of Midwives. In her evidence, Elizabeth stressed that she was "not professional" and her views were only "chiefly based upon my observations", but her presence besides other witnesses such as Rosalind Paget, the first Inspector General of QVJI, and Mrs Henry Smith, one of the founding members of the Midwives' Institute, indicates the esteem in which she was held. The Superintendents described her in 1924 as "the pioneer of county nursing", and Fox acknowledges that, when QVJI first extended into rural areas, "Mrs Malleson's ... innovatory work influenced the Institute's approach to rural nursing".[2]

Elizabeth's belief that RNA Committees and their nurses should "initiate a principle of self-help among the people" was echoed by Amy Hughes as one of the principles of QVJI: "The Queen's Institute ... foster[s] the spirit of independence and help[s] the people to help themselves. ... Every earnest district nurse who sows the seeds of thrift, self-help, self-restraint, self-respect in the round of daily work is a helper ... in solving the social problems of the day." However, this view, whilst acknowledging the widespread problems of poverty, assumed that, in financial terms, the poor needed only guidance in how better to utilise their income. Elizabeth recognised the need for skilled midwifery and nursing accessible to the poor, but when she founded the RNA, she automatically assumed that midwifery fees would be obligatory. She did make provision for a sliding scale of charges dependent on the husband's wage, but a standard national rate was introduced by QVJI. Elizabeth also believed in encouraging "small subscriptions to the nursing fund from the inhabitants of the villages and cottages included in the rural district", and a suggested scale of county fees was included in the Gloucestershire CNA's Second

Annual Report of 1906, ranging from 2s. per annum for Labourers, whose families would then be nursed free, to Tradespeople & Farmers who would pay £1 per annum plus a small nursing fee "at the discretion of the Committee". Midwives (both trained and untrained), private nurses and doctors had, of course, always charged for their services, but the main reason why the poor had previously relied on the village handywoman, willing neighbours and home cures was because they could not afford to pay the professional fees. However well-intentioned any philanthropic scheme may be, if families are living on such small incomes that every penny is budgeted for before it is earned, then financial advice alone is not sufficient. Louise Jermy, a forthright and determined character who always "cut my garment according to the cloth", married an under-gardener in 1911 and gave birth to her first child ten months later. She relates: "I learnt how to lay out my thirteen shillings weekly, so that it kept us in food, and it took me from February 25th, the day I was married, till the end of June, to save one shilling out of it." Lizzie Layton indignantly recalls attending meetings "where ladies came and lectured on the domestic affairs in the workers' homes that it was impossible for them to understand. I have boiled over many times at some of the things I have been obliged to listen to." To such women, preventative education must have seemed more like patronising criticism that emphasised the problems of which they were already only too aware, but without offering practical solutions.[3]

The Ladies Bountiful still believed in *noblesse oblige* and had no wish to change the long-accepted social hierarchy, but this approach risked sanitising and sentimentalising the virtues of poverty. Clearly, this was not their intention: many genuinely sought to improve the lot of the poor, but they attempted to do so without the backing of a government-funded welfare system that provided the poor with the additional means necessary to fulfil their most basic human needs. This belief in charity as the foundation of and sustaining element in a hierarchal society was questioned at Winchcombe in 1903 when the Chairman of the Cottage Hospital Committee stated that he believed philanthropic organisations should be supported by the State. His speech "failed to win assent" and, reporting the Meeting in the Parish Magazine, the local clergyman insisted that it

> might be a good thing for the patients but it would be attended with a very bad effect on us. It would rob us of the training and exercise of those kindly instincts of humanity which we cannot afford to lose. Better to struggle on and with some difficulty keep these charitable institutions going than to have everything done for us by Government.[4]

Apparently, Reverend Taylor believed, it was better to foster a feeling of virtuous benevolence amongst the ruling classes than to provide adequately for the poor.

District nursing represented the professionalisation of such philanthropic efforts in the sense that enlightened Ladies Bountiful progressed from being well-intentioned, benevolent amateurs to becoming well-informed and highly efficient lady administrators who employed trained specialist nurses. However, QVJI remained dependent on charitable donations. In 1909, a year after the introduction of Public Health Work, only approximately 3.5% of the costs of QNs and 1.6% of the costs of VNMs came from public funds in the form of local government grants, as discussed in Chapter Six. Consequently, severe financial difficulties were experienced throughout the organisation and all over the country. As the *Queen's Nurses' Magazine* reported in 1910, "The returns from all County Associations ... agree on this point; it is not the will, but the power that is wanting." The National Insurance Act of 1911 and the introduction of the first Maternity Benefit, both of which were viewed by Elizabeth Malleson as government interference rather than support, did provide some contribution towards home nursing care and midwifery fees, but wartime inflation followed by the depressed economy of the inter-war years exacerbated financial insecurity at every level.[5]

By May 1914, the Training Home at Plaistow was £1,000 in debt and appealed to CNAs for help. They, in turn, wrote to their DNAs for contributions to a fund-raising bazaar. Similarly, the Gloucestershire CNA made a special appeal to all local DNAs for a contribution of £3 towards the training fund for VNMs in 1923. Almost £260 was raised, but some DNAs "expressed regret that, owing to their own financial position, it was impossible for them to make any contribution". Tibberton DNA was unable to contribute as their bank account was overdrawn, and as detailed in Chapter Six, the CNA turned down their request for a grant as it had insufficient funds to cover all DNA deficits. In fact, the CNA had made its appeal in the knowledge that, as it had reported the previous year, "the terrible amount of unemployment and the great drop in Agricultural wages have made it very difficult for the local Associations to raise the necessary funds". It was a vicious circle and by 1925 the CNA faced a deficit of £400. To augment the county funds, a Grand Bazaar & Concert were held at Cheltenham Town Hall in November 1925 at which more than £2,500 was raised. The success of this fund-raising event was credited to the "influential Committee of ladies from different parts of the County", which indicates the continued importance of the social elite in rural areas. Keen public interest and media publicity were ensured by the presence of HRH the Duchess of York as Guest of Honour. Her visit was deemed to merit a full page of enthusiastic and patriotic reports in the local newspaper, with a four page supplement of photographs, describing how "the flags and pennants in the Promenade lent colour to the scene, and Cheltenham became gay, and proud, and happy in its welcome to one of the most charming and popular members of the Royal House".[6]

It is clear that much of the success of QVJI's work was due to the influence, skill and determination of the middle and upper class ladies who devoted themselves to the needs of the poor. Personally, they derived a sense of worth and achievement in their administrative roles, but the work was constantly hampered by financial restraints, themselves arising from the persistent belief that government intervention would deprive poor families of the incentive to support themselves. In the circumstances, it is remarkable that they achieved so much: by 1925, it was estimated that district nursing was available to 75% of the population of England and Wales, a figure that reflects not only the altruism of the lady administrators, but also the dedication of the nurses themselves.

By that time, a new era had begun for the entire nursing profession, with the introduction of the Registration Act of 1919. At a Conference of Superintendents in 1922, Miss Peterkin, then Superintendent General of QVJI, gave a talk on the subject of State Registration, stating that, "so far Queen's Nurses had registered better than any others, and that is as it ought to be". Her comment leaves no doubt that the district nurses regarded their work as of at least equal importance to hospital nursing and viewed the State Register as an opportunity to publicly and professionally establish their role as central to the health and welfare of the nation.[7]

Whilst the advent of the Register, thirty years after it was first proposed, standardised hospital training, it did little to improve the working conditions of hospital nurses. At a time when other young women were beginning to experience greater freedom and wider opportunities, hospital nursing still involved hard physical work, strict discipline and personal restrictions. As Ruth Adam says, "The bitter truth was that in the only profession run by women almost entirely for women, the girl beginners were exploited in a way which would have provided wonderful ammunition for the Women's Movement if only it had been arranged by men."[8] It is little wonder that many of the nurses who completed their training then wished to escape the restrictions of hospital life. Private nursing remained an option, whilst nursing in the colonies offered the opportunity to travel, as did military nursing, particularly after the founding of Queen's Alexandra's Imperial Military Nursing Service in 1902. Rural district nursing was, without doubt, physically demanding, as the number of nurses who resigned on health grounds confirms, but the combination of midwifery with general nursing offered wider experience and the introduction of Public Health Work offered new opportunities. Whilst the nurses worked under the supervision of their DNA Committees, in co-operation with local doctors, and were subject to inspection both locally by the County Superintendent and nationally by QVJI Inspectors, in their day-to-day duties they worked alone. Clearly, some nurses were overwhelmed by such responsibility and isolation, but those who found the work rewarding and enjoyed the independent lifestyle, were able to develop a warm relationship with their poor patients that encompassed every stage and aspect of family life.

However, the problems of finance persisted, with many rural areas unable to raise sufficient funds to employ a QN, though this fact alone does not account for the predominance of VNMs: the nature of the work and its centrality to community life offered security and self-respect to rural working class women. Hospital nurses, as well as women teachers and civil servants, were expected to resign on marriage, but VNMs included both women who were married before or after their training and widows with children to support. Before the formation of the RNA, many untrained women had supplemented midwifery with other, unskilled work, but Elizabeth Malleson envisaged trained local women who could earn their living and serve their community solely by combining midwifery and general nursing. Though Elizabeth herself changed her mind and came to believe that middle and upper class lady nurses would set a better example and exert a greater influence on the poor, it was her original idea that came to predominate in rural areas.

The district nurses were not, of course, the only midwives available to the rural poor. The Midwives Act of 1902 made provision for *bona fide* and certificated midwives to practise independently, though under local authority inspection. Gloucestershire was one of several counties where the role of Inspector of Midwives became part of the duties of the County Superintendent and her Assistants. This arrangement ensured that standards were maintained, and was regarded by the CNA Committee "as marking an important advance in the public recognition of the necessity of systematic training and supervision in Maternity Nursing, and as testifying to the position which the Association has already won for itself in the County".[9] Thus, independent midwives continued to work, especially in the most isolated and remote areas of the county, where the population was too small to support either a QN or VNM, and which, from their geographical position, could not be included in existing districts. QVJI offered professional midwifery and nursing care to the poor, but through sheer necessity, the new and a standardised, improved traditional system co-existed in rural counties.

In addition, many of the rural poor still clung to their old ways and beliefs, particularly where the use of home remedies was concerned. Foley recalls that, in the Forest of Dean after World War 1, the poor still "dreaded being taken to the workhouse" and her family rarely sought professional help:

> Mostly our Dad cured us with his home-made potions. He gathered elderflower, yarrow, camomile, and other wild herbs, dried them and stored them in brown paper bags for his bitter brews. Constipation, coughs, colic, sickness, diarrhoea, sores, fever, delirium - whatever we had, out came the dreaded brown jug, and on the hob it went with its infusion of herbs.

Neighbourliness also remained an important and sustaining element in village life. When Louise Jermy's husband died of double pneumonia in 1921, "one of my neighbours, Mrs Chambers, was with me all that last dreadful night, and another, Mrs Allen, was with me when he died. They did all that had to be done." Her husband had been born in the village, and the local men, his lifelong friends, gave £10 from their harvest wages to pay for the funeral and to help support his widow and two young sons.[10]

Whilst the 'village spirit' survived, Gerard suggests that relations between Lady Bountiful and the poor "sometimes became more formal and distant" when the needs of the latter were served by DNAs, as the administrative work this involved left less time for personal visiting. It is, of course, impossible to generalise on this point, as the success of the relationship had always, to a great extent, depended on the attitude and personality of the individual Lady Bountiful, which could enhance both the landowning family's power in, and the cohesiveness of, the community. In the inter-war years of recession, the rural poor still valued the benevolence of paternalism if it promoted dignity and self-respect: on the day John Jermy died, the local Squire passed by the family's cottage and, seeing the newly-widowed Louise, "he lifted his hat ... and I noticed that he did not replace his hat till he had passed the house some little way, and as I watched him, I thought his graceful act of respect for his dead servant would not have disgraced a prince." Louise was allowed to continue living in the cottage, and the Lady of the Manor, who she recalls, "always treated me with real kindness", employed her as the estate laundress so she could "bring up my boys free from the parish".[11]

In a novel published posthumously, Flora Thompson mourned the passing of such benevolent Ladies of the Manor and of the village handywomen, the former "kind though exacting employers, bounteous to the poor in their own villages", the latter who, "learned only in country lore and the Holy Scriptures, ... used their spare energy in helping their neighbours, ... slapped life into the newly born and sped the dying with words of homely comfort". In their time, they had served their community well, but "there is no place for Lady Bountiful or Dame Smith in this modern world".[12] Their place was taken by the lady administrator and the district nurse.

Through running CNAs and DNAs, the lady administrators redefined their own role, whilst maintaining their status, and it is clear from surviving records that the rural poor did benefit from and appreciated their work for QVJI. In the face of economic, geographical and human realities, the district nurses they employed delivered a service that was both professional and acceptable, but not optimal. It was not part of their official aims to help poor women have fewer babies, only to raise healthier children; their midwifery skills did not include the administration of pain relief during childbirth; health education did not ensure that daughters understood their bodies and were thus mentally and emotionally prepared for puberty, marriage and motherhood; advice on feeding and clothing a family did not, in itself, guarantee an income sufficient to put the theory into practice; and trained nursing care did nothing to solve the working and living conditions of the poor that exacerbated the severity and spread of many common illnesses. Nevertheless, within the confines of the social policies of the times and through co-operation with other social agencies, the district nurses took a greater level and scope of nursing, midwifery and welfare care into the homes of the rural poor than had ever been available to them before.

Notes

1. Celia Davies, 'The Contemporary Challenge in Nursing History' in *Rewriting Nursing History,* ed. by Celia Davies (London: Croom Helm, 1980), pp.11-17.
   Christopher Maggs, 'A New History of Nursing: The State of the Art', *Nursing Times,* August 14 1985, 36-37.
   Anne Summers, 'A Home from Home: Women's Philanthropic Work in the Nineteenth Century' in *Fit Work for Women,* ed. by Sandra Burman (London: Croom Helm, 1979), pp.33-63.
2. Hope Malleson, *Elizabeth Malleson: A Memoir* (Printed for Private Circulation, 1926), pp.83, 92, 217 & 238.
   GRO D4057/14 Gotherington album of documents re formation of the RNA 1884-94.
   Some Queen's Superintendents, *Handbook for Queen's Nurses* (London: Scientific Press, 1924), p.10.
   Enid Fox, *District Nursing & the Work of District Nursing Associations in England & Wales, 1900-48* (PhD Thesis, London University, 1993), p.88.
3. *British Medical Journal,* letter from Mrs Malleson, August 30 1890, p.540.
   Amy Hughes, 'The Origin, Growth, & Present Status of District Nursing in England', *The Nursing Record & Hospital World,* May 17 1902, 391-3.
   GRO D4057/1 Gloucestershire CNA Annual Reports 1905-31.
   Louise Jermy, *The Memories of a Working Woman* (Norwich: Goose, 1934), pp.168 & 180.
   Lizzie Layton, 'Memories of Seventy Years' in *Life As We Have Known It by Co-operative Working Women,* ed. by Margaret Llewelyn Davies (London: Virago, 1977 edition; first published 1931), pp.1-55.
4. CRL 336G283 *Winchcombe Parish Magazine,* January 1900-December 1908.
5. Unattributed, 'County Nursing Associations & Their Work', *Queen's Nurses' Magazine,* Vol V11 Part 1 (April 1910), 9-11.
6. GRO D2410 Minutes of Gloucestershire CNA 1904-28.
   GRO D4057/1.
   Gloucestershire Echo, November 17 1925, p.6, c.2-5.
7. Unattributed, 'Reports of Queen's Superintendents' Annual Conference', *QNM*, Vol X1X Part 2 (1922), 25-32.
8. Ruth Adam, *A Woman's Place 1910-1975* (New York: Norton, 1977), p.80.
   See also Carrie Howse, 'Registration: A Minor Victory?', *Nursing Times,*'Vol 85, No 49 (December 6-12 1989), 32-34.
9. GRO D4057/1.
10. Winifred Foley, *A Child in the Forest* (London: British Broadcasting Corporation, 1974), pp.98-9.
    Jermy, *Memories,* pp.182-3.

11. Jessica Gerard, 'Lady Bountiful: Women of the Landed Classes & Rural Philanthropy', *Victorian Studies,* Vol 30 (Winter 1987), 183-210. Jermy, *Memories,* pp.183 & 186.
12. Flora Thompson, *Still Glides the Stream* (Oxford University Press, 1981 edition; first published 1948), pp.42-3.

BIBLIOGRAPHY

Documents

CMAC =	Contemporary Medical Archives Centre, Wellcome Institute, London
CRL =	Cheltenham Reference Library
GRO =	Gloucestershire Record Office

British Library Add45808, F119-127 & F163-165v Letters from Elizabeth Malleson to Florence Nightingale 1888.

CMAC Records of Queen's Nurses.

CRL 61G942CHA Charlton Kings Local History Society Bulletins.

CRL 336G283 Winchcombe Parish Magazine 1900-08.

CRL 336G914 The Winchcombe & Sudeley Record 1890-96.

GRO D1070/VII/91 Fairford Cottage Hospital Annual Reports 1870-1923.

GRO D2410 Minutes of Gloucestershire CNA 1904-28.

GRO D2429/4 Cinderford Infant Welfare Centre Minutes Book 1915-30.

GRO D2465 4/32 & 4/33 Cheltenham DNA Annual Reports 1880-1905 & 1907-31, including Balance Sheets for Charlton Kings, Staverton & Shurdington DNAs 1911-16.

GRO D2465 4/35 Cheltenham DNA Correspondence 1892-1917.

GRO D2752 4/12 & 4/13 Walwins of Gloucester Prescription Books 1877-82.

GRO D2774 3/1 Stroud DNA Annual Reports 1895-1946.

GRO D2774 6/1 Papers concerning Stroud DNA 1893-5.

GRO D3548 3/1 Nailsworth DNA Annual Reports 1900-48.

GRO D3548 5/2 Nailsworth DNA Register of Cases 1907.

GRO D3548 6/1 Bundle of 9 miscellaneous documents 1896-1928.

GRO D3549 Papers of Lloyd Baker family, Hardwicke Court, Glos.

GRO D4057/1 Gloucestershire CNA Annual Reports 1905-31.

GRO D4057/3 Gloucestershire CNA correspondence 1910-11.

GRO D4057/6 Gloucestershire County Council Co-ordination of Nursing 1926.

GRO D4057/14 Gotherington album of documents re formation of the RNA 1884-94.

GRO D4057/15 Gotherington DNA Annual Reports 1890-1916.

GRO D4057/19 Staverton Parish Magazine 1902.

GRO D4277 12/1 Tibberton DNA Minutes Book 1918-26.

GRO D4277 12/2 Tibberton DNA Accounts Book 1922-26.

GRO D4457/1 Thompson of Tetbury Customers' Orders 1878-1904.

GRO D5792 Sellors of Tewkesbury Medical Recipes 1870-85.

GRO D6043 1/18 Campden DNA List of furniture & effects in Nurse's House 1903.
GRO G/SO/87 Chipping Sodbury Workhouse Punishment Books 1876-1947.
GRO G/STR/93 Stroud Union Workhouse Chaplain's Report Book 1847-91.
GRO G/TET/145/1 Tetbury District Medical Relief Book 1876-81.
GRO G/TEW/87 Tewkesbury Union Workhouse Punishment Books 1853-1929.
GRO G/WI/95/13 Winchcombe Union Workhouse Master's Journal 1880.
GRO HO2 8/2 Bourton-on-the-Water Cottage Hospital Annual Reports 1875-84.
GRO HO3 8/9 Cheltenham Hospital Annual Reports 1880-89.
GRO HO30 25/1 Reminiscences about foundation of Moreton-in-Marsh Cottage Hospital by Miss Rebecca Horne, the first Matron.
GRO HO40 8/2 Tetbury Cottage Hospital Annual Reports 1871-91.
GRO P244a MI 13/1 Painswick DNA Minutes 1900-20.
GRO P347 MI 3/1 Upton St Leonards DNA Minutes 1901-09.
GRO P347 MI 3/5 Upton St Leonards DNA Inventory of Nurse's Home 1908.
Hicks-Beach private family papers, courtesy of Lord St Aldwyn, Williamstrip Park, Nr Cirencester, Glos.

Journals and Newspapers

British Medical Journal
Cheltenham Chronicle & Gloucestershire Graphic
Cheltenham Examiner
Gloucestershire Echo
Lancet
Nursing Record
Queen's Nurses' Magazine
The Times

Books and Articles

Abel-Smith, Brian, *A History of the Nursing Profession* (London: Heinemann, 1960).
Adam, Ruth, *A Woman's Place 1910-1975* (New York: Norton, 1977).
Aldred, David H. (ed.), Gotherington Area Local History Society, *Gotherington: The History of a Village* (Stroud: Sutton, 1993).
Allan, Peta & Jolley, Moya (eds.), *Nursing, Midwifery and Health Visiting since 1900* (London: Faber, 1982).

Baly, Monica E., *Florence Nightingale and the Nursing Legacy* (London: Croom Helm, 1986).
Baly, Monica E., *A History of the Queen's Nursing Institute* (Beckenham: Croom Helm, 1987).
Baly, Monica E., *Nursing and Social Change* (London: Routledge, 1995).
Bell, Lady Florence, *At the Works: A Study of a Manufacturing Town* (London: Virago, 1985 edition; first published 1907).
Berridge, Virginia, 'Health and Medicine' in *The Cambridge Social History of Britain 1750-1950: Vol. 3 Social Agencies and Institutions,* ed. by F.M.L. Thompson (Cambridge University Press, 1990), pp.171-242.
Bingham, Stella, *Ministering Angels* (London: Osprey, 1979).
Bowman, Gerald, *The Lamp and the Book: The Story of the RCN, 1916-1966* (London: Queen Anne Press, 1967).
Branca, Patricia, *Silent Sisterhood: Middle-Class Women in the Victorian Home* (London: Croom Helm, 1975).
Brookes, Barbara, 'Women and Reproduction 1860-1939' in *Labour and Love: Women's Experience of Home and Family 1850-1940,* ed. by Jane Lewis (Oxford: Blackwell, 1986), pp.149-71.
Bulley, Miss A. Amy & Whitley, Miss Margaret, *Women's Work* (London: Methuen, 1894).
Burdett-Coutts, Angela (ed.), *Woman's Mission: A Series of Congress Papers on the Philanthropic Work of Women by Eminent Writers* (London: Sampson Low, Marston, 1893).
Chamberlain, Mary, *Fenwomen: A Portrait of Women in an English Village* (London: Virago, 1975).
Chamberlain, Mary, *Old Wives' Tales: Their History, Remedies and Spells* (London: Virago, 1981).
Cope, Zachary, 'The Early History of District Nursing', *Nursing Times*, 12 August 1955, 844-7.
Cowell, Betty & Wainwright, David, *Behind the Blue Door: The History of the Royal College of Midwives, 1881-1981* (London: Bailliere Tindall, 1981).
Craven, Florence, *A Guide to District Nurses and Home Nursing* (London: MacMillan, 1894).
Davidoff, Leonore & Hall, Catherine, *Family Fortunes: Men and Women of the English Middle Class 1780-1850* (London: Century Hutchison, 1987).
Davies, Celia, 'The Contemporary Challenge in Nursing History' in *Rewriting Nursing History,* ed. by Celia Davies (London: Croom Helm, 1980), pp.11-17.
Davies, Margaret Llewelyn (ed.), *Maternity: Letters from Working Women collected by The Women's Co-operative Guild* (London: Virago, 1978 edition; first published 1915).

Davies, Margaret Llewelyn (ed.), *Life As We Have Known It by Co-operative Working Women* (London: Virago, 1977 edition; first published 1931).
Dingwall, Robert, Rafferty, Anne Marie & Webster, Charles, *An Introduction to the Social History of Nursing* (London: Routledge, 1988).
Donnison, Jean, *Midwives and Medical Men: A History of Inter-Professional Rivalries and Women's Rights* (New York: Schocken Books, 1977).
Evans, George Ewart, *Where Beards Wag All* (London: Faber & Faber, 1970).
Foley, Winifred, *A Child in the Forest* (London: British Broadcasting Corporation, 1974).
Fox, Enid Nora, *District Nursing and the Work of District Nursing Associations in England and Wales, 1900-48* (PhD Thesis, London University, 1993).
Fox, E.N., 'Universal Health Care and Self-Help: Paying for District Nursing before the National Health Service', *Twentieth Century British History,* Vol. 7, No. 1 (1996), 83-109.
Fraser, Flora, *The English Gentlewoman* (London: Guild Publishing, 1987).
Gerard, Jessica, 'Lady Bountiful: Women of the Landed Classes and Rural Philanthropy', *Victorian Studies*, Vol. 30 (Winter 1987), 183-210.
Gleadle, Kathryn, *The Early Feminists: Radical Unitarians and the Emergence of the Women's Rights Movement, 1831-51* (London: Macmillan, 1995).
Hall, Catherine, 'The Early Formation of Victorian Domestic Ideology' in *Fit Work for Women*, ed. by Sandra Burman (London: Croom Helm, 1979), pp.15-32.
Hardy, Gwen, *William Rathbone and the Early History of District Nursing* (Ormskirk: Hesketh, 1981).
Herstein, Sheila R., *A Mid-Victorian Feminist: Barbara Leigh Smith Bodichon* (New Haven: Yale University Press, 1985).
Hirsch, Pam, *Barbara Leigh Smith Bodichon 1827-1891: Feminist, Artist and Rebel* (London: Chatto & Windus, 1998).
Holcombe, Lee, *Victorian Ladies at Work* (Newton Abbot: David & Charles, 1973).
Holdsworth, Angela, *Out of the Doll's House: The Story of Women in the Twentieth Century* (London: BBC Books, 1988).
Horn, Pamela, *Labouring Life in the Victorian Countryside* (Dublin: Gill & Macmillan, 1976).
Horn, Pamela, *The Changing Countryside in Victorian and Edwardian England and Wales* (London: Athlone, 1984).
Horn, Pamela, *The Rise and Fall of the Victorian Servant* (Stroud: Sutton, 1990).

Horn, Pamela, *Ladies of the Manor: Wives and Daughters in Country-House Society 1830-1918* (Stroud: Sutton, 1991).
Horn, Pamela, *Women in the 1920s* (Stroud: Sutton, 1995).
Howse, Carrie, 'VADs at War', *Nursing Times,* Vol. 80, No. 31 (1-7 August 1984), 36-8.
Howse, Carrie, 'Registration: A Minor Victory?', *Nursing Times,* Vol. 85, No. 49 (6-12 December 1989), 32-4.
Howse, Carrie, 'From Lady Bountiful to Lady Administrator: Women and the Administration of Rural District Nursing in England, 1880-1925', *Women's History Review,* Vol. 15, No. 3 (July 2006), 423-41.
Howse, Carrie, '"The Ultimate Destination of all Nursing": The Development of District Nursing in England, 1880-1925', *Nursing History Review,* Vol. 15 (2007), 65-94.
Hunt, Agnes, *Reminiscences* (Shrewsbury: Wilding, 1935).
Jermy, Louise, *The Memories of a Working Woman* (Norwich: Goose, 1934).
Langland, Elizabeth, *Nobody's Angels: Middle-class Women and Domestic Ideology in Victorian Culture* (New York: Cornell University Press, 1995).
Lewis, Jane, *The Politics of Motherhood: Child and Maternal Welfare in England, 1900-1939* (London: Croom Helm, 1980).
Lewis, Jane, *Women in England 1870-1950: Sexual Divisions and Social Change* (Brighton: Wheatsheaf Books, 1984).
Loane, Margaret, *Outlines of Routine in District Nursing* (London: Scientific Press, 1905).
McKibbin, Ross, *The Ideologies of Class* (Oxford University Press, 1991).
Maggs, Christopher J., *The Origins of General Nursing* (Beckenham: Croom Helm: 1983).
Maggs, Christopher, 'Made, Not Born', *Nursing Times,* Vol. 80, No. 38 (19-25 September 1984), 31-4.
Maggs, Christopher, 'A New History of Nursing: The State of the Art', *Nursing Times,* 14 August 1985, 36-7.
Malleson, Hope, *Elizabeth Malleson: A Memoir* (Printed for Private Circulation, 1926).
Marwick, Arthur, *Women at War 1914-1918* (Glasgow: Fontana, 1977).
Millett, Kate, 'The Debate over Women: Ruskin versus Mill' in *Suffer and Be Still: Women in the Victorian Age,* ed. by Martha Vicinus (London: Methuen, 1972), pp.121-39.
Mingay, G.E., *Rural Life in Victorian England* (Stroud: Sutton, 1976).
Moore, Judith, *A Zeal for Responsibility: The Struggle for Professional Nursing in Victorian England, 1868-1883* (University of Georgia Press, 1988).

Morley, Edith J. (ed.), *Women Workers in Seven Professions: A Survey of their Economic Conditions and Prospects* (London: Routledge, 1915).
Nash, Rosalind (ed.), *Florence Nightingale to her Nurses: A Selection from Miss Nightingale's Addresses to Probationers and Nurses of the Nightingale School at St Thomas's Hospital, 1872-1888* (London: MacMillan, 1914).
Nightingale, Florence, *Notes on Nursing* (Glasgow: Blackie, 1974 edition; first published 1859).
Peterson, M. Jeanne, 'The Victorian Governess: Status Incongruence in Family and Society' in *Suffer and Be Still: Women in the Victorian Age*, ed. by Martha Vicinus (London: Methuen, 1972), pp.3-19.
Powell, Margaret, *Below Stairs* (London: Pan Books, 1970 edition; first published 1968).
Powell, Margaret, *Climbing the Stairs* (London: Pan Books, 1969).
Powell, Margaret, *My Mother and I* (London: Pan Books, 1974 edition; first published, 1972).
Prochaska, F.K., *Women and Philanthropy in Nineteenth Century England* (Oxford University Press, 1980).
Reeves, Maud Pember, *Round About a Pound a Week* (London: Virago, 1979 edition; first published 1913).
Roberts, Elizabeth, *A Woman's Place: An Oral History of Working-Class Women 1890-1940* (Oxford: Blackwell, 1984).
Rose, Walter, *Good Neighbours: Some Recollections of an English Village and its People* (Cambridge University Press, 1942).
Some Queen's Superintendents, *Handbook for Queen's Nurses* (London: Scientific Press, 1924).
Stocks, Mary, *A Hundred Years of District Nursing* (London: Allen & Unwin, 1960).
Summers, Anne, 'A Home from Home: Women's Philanthropic Work in the Nineteenth Century' in *Fit Work for Women*, ed. by Sandra Burman (London: Croom Helm, 1979), pp.33-63.
Summers, Anne, *Angels and Citizens: British Women as Military Nurses 1854-1914* (London: Routledge, 1988).
Summers, Anne, 'The Costs and Benefits of Caring: Nursing Charities, c1830-c1860' in *Medicine and Charity Before the Welfare State*, ed. by Jonathan Barry & Colin Jones (London: Routledge, 1991), pp.133-48.
Thompson, Flora, *Lark Rise to Candleford* (Harmondsworth: Penguin, 1973 edition; first published in three parts 1939-43).
Thompson, Flora, *Still Glides the Stream* (Oxford University Press, 1981 edition; first published 1948).
Towler, Jean & Bramall, Joan, *Midwives in History and Society* (London: Croom Helm, 1986).

Versluysen, Margaret Connor, 'Old Wives' Tales? Women Healers in English History' in *Rewriting Nursing History*, ed. by Celia Davies (London: Croom Helm, 1980), pp.175-99.

Vicinus, Martha, *Independent Women: Work and Community for Single Women 1850-1920* (London: Virago, 1985).

Vicinus, Martha & Nergaard, Bea (eds.), *Ever Yours, Florence Nightingale: Selected Letters* (London: Virago, 1989).

White, Rosemary, *Social Change and the Development of the Nursing Profession* (London: Kimpton, 1978).

Williams, A. Susan, *Ladies of Influence: Women of the Elite in Interwar Britain* (London: Penguin, 2001).

Woodham-Smith, Cecil, *Florence Nightingale* (London: Book Club Associates, 1972 edition, first published 1950).

INDEX

INDEX

INDEX

INDEX

INDEX

AUTHOR

Carrie Howse is a women's health and welfare historian with a particular interest in the history of nursing, having been a nurse herself in the 1970s. For more than twenty years, she has written historical features, nursing-related articles and academic papers for journals including the *Nursing Times*, *Nursing Standard*, *Nursing History Review* and *Women's History Review*. She has a PhD from the University of Gloucestershire (2004), on which this, her first, book is based. She has won the following awards for her research and writing:

2001 Highly Commended, Clare Evans Prize
2003 Finalist, GRCC Bryan Jerrard Award
2005 Winner, AAHN Postdoctoral Award
2007 Second place, BALH Local History Award
2007 Winner, AAHN Mary Adelaide Nutting Award
2007 Winner GRCC Bryan Jerrard Award

Dr Howse can be contacted by email: **carrievcm@fsmail.net**